KAUN BANEGA CROREPATI

KAUN BANEGA CROREPATI

Edited and Compiled by
Siddhartha Basu

Rupa . Co

First Published 2010
Second Impression 2010

Published by
Rupa Publications India Pvt. Ltd.
7/16, Ansari Road, Daryaganj
New Delhi 110 002

Sales Centres:

Allahabad Bengaluru Chandigarh Chennai
Hyderabad Jaipur Kathmandu
Kolkata Mumbai

Edited and compiled by – Siddhartha Basu
Content Editor – Bhaskar Jyoti Dey
Copy Editor – Debarati Sengupta
Director, Consumer Product Licensing – David Christopher
Product and Brand Manager – Lisa O'Connell

Typeset by
Mindways Design
1410 Chiranjiv Tower,
43 Nehru Place
New Delhi 110 019

Printed in India by
Nutech Photolithographers
B-240, Okhla Industrial Area, Phase-I
New Delhi 110 020, India

CONTENTS

Foreword

'Ek Chidiya Chonch Mein Tinka Liye Jo Jaa Rahi Thi,
Woh Sahaj Mein Hi Pawan Unchaas Ko Neecha Dikhati'

These lines penned by my father reiterate the spirit of the human nature.

Kaun Banega Crorepati is not about the questions. It is not about the fame on national television and it is most definitely not about the money. The show is about fair play, sportsmanship and the people. People who have defied all odds to be on the show, are self-assured and determined to emerge as winners. They are convinced and will not let anybody make them believe otherwise.

Contestants I meet on the show come from varied backgrounds and it is most humbling to interact with them and listen to their stories. Some of these people inspire me in ways I wouldn't think possible. Over the last forty decades I have grown only because of the love of these people and it feels good to be on the show amongst them, to talk to them and to laugh with them. I love being the messenger of good fortune every time they win.

If being a contestant and winning a crore is tough, then being the one who has to break that dream is definitely tougher. How does one muster enough courage to shatter hopes? And to tell a contestant that he has earned from the last ten levels but one wrong move and he has come crashing down, and that he hasn't played well enough to go ahead to the next round.

The world of questions is fascinating. The more questions I ask, the more it makes me realise how little we know and how important it is to travel, question, ponder and keep our minds open.

For me, *Kaun Banega Crorepati* has been a learning experience. The teams at Synergy and Sony remind me that you do not always have to be the lead player to steal the show. The contestants I have met and the stories I have heard remind me always that everything we face in life only helps us build character and that most problems are only situations. And that if it is too difficult to laugh at these situations, there indeed is a problem.

Here's looking forward to many more fascinating years of answers. And like I keep saying '*koi bhi sawaal chhota nahin hota*'.

Amitabh Bachchan

Preface

Kaun Banega Crorepati was a communicator's dream come true, to feel the pulse of the public in sync with the show for every micro second of its run. '*Nau baj gaye kya?*' was the common buzz as the hour approached. As the clock would strike 9, streets would empty, restaurants would lose business, night shows would take a beating, and people would scramble home to their telly with their families. You could hear the signature tune booming out of homes, as the rich, gravely voice of the host took over. Viewers hung on to every twist and turn of the contest's journey. The first contestant, the first *lakhpati*, the first to win 25 lakhs, 50 lakhs – every milestone became front page news. And then came along the Crorepati. Ratings shot through the roof. Here was a landmark show, a rare, once-in-a-lifetime experience.

All said and done, it was a game of questions and answers, that's what lay at the heart of the show. And setting questions for KBC posed a unique set of challenges. The contestants came from everywhere, with widely varying levels of education, background, interests and awareness. The quiz had to be all things to all people. The key was to manage enough range to have a sporting set of questions for every contestant.

That's how *Q&A* became the vital plot device and title of Vikas Swarup's book, which formed the basis of the multiple Oscar award winning *Slumdog Millionaire*. In a way, the movie was an ultimate tribute to the KBC phenomena, an acknowledgement and showcase of the impact it had in India, with its story of an underdog contestant on the show.

The movie, in turn, has fuelled renewed interest in the show and energised it overseas. There are a number of innovations in format and presentation. The ascent is now faster and more nerve wracking. There are just twelve questions. There is a timer. There are new lifelines. But the essence remains as ever, the magic is the same.

It's in this new avatar that KBC is being reborn on Sony, who are sparing no effort in making it a vibrant and memorable experience for viewers, with Amitabh Bachchan at the helm as host. All thanks to the entire team at Sony Entertainment Television for believing in the power of the show and bringing it back on air, most notably N.P. Singh and Ajit Thakur. Thanks too to Divya Morparia of Sony, David Cristopher and Lisa O'Connell from 2waytraffic, in helping us come out with the first edition of the book based on the show.

This book commemorates the return of KBC, even as it reprises moments of the much loved show, with questions culled from its past, designed to provide an accessible and rich gaming experience to readers, and will hopefully please, tease and tantalise.

I'd like to thank all the question-writers and contributors, too numerous to name, who pitched in with their imagination and labour to make this quiz pool. I'd also like to thank each and every one otherwise involved in the making of KBC, most of all my co-producers, my wife Anita, and Karun Prabhakar.

It's a pleasure and privilege to be a part of a historic television show, and this is an invitation to readers and viewers to share that experience. Because once again it's time for a celebration of knowledge and awareness, and to re-discover that '*koi bhi sawaal chhota nahin hota*'.

Siddhartha Basu
BIG Synergy

How to Play

Bite your nails, scratch your head and brace yourself for *Kaun Banega Crorepati – The Official Book*. This book is sure to test you to your absolute limits! Earn yourself a place in the hot seat by making it quickest through the Fastest Finger First round and answer questions across twelve levels. You could challenge yourself or invite some friends and see who has got the brawniest brain!

For 1 Player

Just like the show *Kaun Banega Crorepati*, the aim of the game is to reach ₹1 Crore. Before you can even think about the twelve levels, you must first correctly answer a question from the Fastest Finger First section. You have just thirty seconds to put the letters in the correct order. When time's up, follow the page reference at the foot of the page to find out if you can take your place in the hot seat and begin your climb!

Once in the hot seat

Start with a question worth ₹5,000 and once you have decided on your final answer (and you are absolutely sure...) follow the page reference at the foot of the page to find out if you've won. If your answer is correct, you can play the next round of ₹10,000, and so on up the tree. The page where each money level begins is listed in the answer section.

As on the programme, you have three lifelines to help you on your way to ₹1 Crore. These are, of course, optional but each of them can only be used once, so only use them when you really need to.

Fifty-Fifty

This option takes away two incorrect answers leaving the correct answer and one incorrect answer remaining; a page reference at the bottom of each page will direct you to the relevant section.

Ask the Audience

This works in exactly the same way as on *Kaun Banega Crorepati,* except we've asked the audience so you don't have to! Simply follow the page reference at the bottom of each page to find out what the audience thought. In the end, however, the final decision is yours.

Phone a Friend

If you have a telephone handy (and a willing friend!) ring him/her up to help you out. You have thirty seconds (no cheating, now...) to read the question to your friend and for them to tell you what they think the answer is. If there's someone else around, ask if they can time it for you.

If you answer incorrectly, you are out of the game. ₹10,000 and ₹3,20,000 are 'safe havens' so if you answer a question incorrectly and you have not reached ₹10,000, then not only are you out of the game but you won't have won anything either. If you have reached one (or both) of these havens and you answer a question incorrectly, then you are out of the game but you will have won the value of the previous haven you have reached. If, at any point during the game, you are unsure of an answer and don't want to risk being out of the game by answering incorrectly, then you can 'stick' at the amount you have won so far and that will be your final score. As you play, use the score sheet at the back of the book to keep a running record of the amount you have won and the lifelines you have used.

For 2-5 Players

Players should take turns at being the host and playing 'Amitabh Bachchan' and posing questions to the other contestant/s. The rules are the same as for a single player (see pages xi-xii). If someone reaches ₹1 Crore, that person is the winner and the game is over. Otherwise, whoever has won the most money when everyone else is out is the winner.

Are you ready to play? Good. We're sure we don't need to tell you to think very carefully before you give your final answer. Good luck and be sure to remember – it's only easy if you know the answer!

Fastest Finger First

Fastest Finger First

1

Arrange these beauty queens in the chronological order in which they were crowned Miss World.

A: Reita Faria

B: Priyanka Chopra

C: Aishwarya Rai

D: Diana Hayden

2

Put these surnames in the serial order in which they would appear in a telephone directory.

A: Tendulkar

B: Ganguly

C: Kambli

D: Kumble

3

Starting with the earliest, arrange these emperors in chronological order.

A: Humayun

B: Jahangir

C: Babur

D: Akbar

4

Arrange the following classical dances of India from north to south.

A: Odissi

B: Kuchipudi

C: Kathak

D: Kathakali

5

Arrange these units of measurement in increasing order of their numerical value.

A: Lakh

B: Arab

C: Crore

D: Kharab

Turn to the answer section on page 227 to see if you've earned a place in the hot seat

6

Arrange the following imaginary lines from north to south.

A: Tropic of Cancer
B: Arctic Circle
C: Tropic of Capricorn
D: Equator

7

Starting with the earliest, arrange these women oriented films in order of their release.

A: Mother India
B: Dor
C: Achhut Kanya
D: Pakeezah

8

Starting from the north, going south, arrange these holy places of the Char Dham in order.

A: Badrinath
B: Rameshwaram
C: Jagannath Puri
D: Dwarka

9

Arrange these tennis players in the order in which they first won the Wimbledon Singles title.

A: Bjorn Borg
B: Rod Laver
C: Boris Becker
D: Pete Sampras

10

Starting from the largest, arrange these oceans in decreasing order of size.

A: Pacific Ocean
B: Atlantic Ocean
C: Indian Ocean
D: Arctic Ocean

Turn to the answer section on page 227 to see if you've earned a place in the hot seat

11

Arrange these vehicles in the increasing order of their authorised passenger carrying capacity.

A: Bus
B: Auto Rickshaw
C: Bicycle
D: Boeing 747

12

Arrange these traditional Indian sarees from north to south.

A: Banarasi
B: Paithani
C: Maheshwari
D: Kanchipuram

13

Starting with the most frequent, arrange these events in the decreasing frequency of their occurrence.

A: Lok Sabha Session
B: Census
C: Presidential Elections
D: Republic Day Parade

14

Arrange these towns by the order in which the Yamuna flows past them.

A: Allahabad
B: Mathura
C: Delhi
D: Agra

15

Starting with the earliest, arrange these people in the order in which they won the Nobel Prize.

A: Amartya Sen
B: Rabindranath Tagore
C: Mother Teresa
D: C V Raman

Turn to the answer section on page 227 to see if you've earned a place in the hot seat

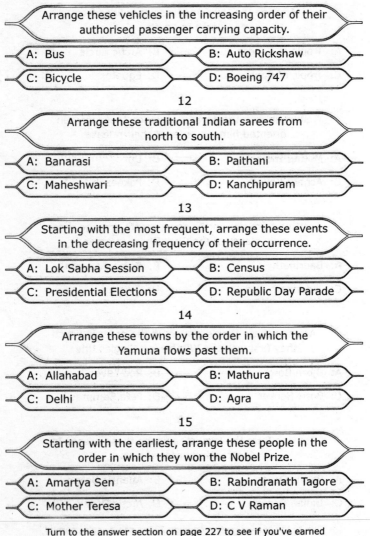

16

Starting from the smallest, arrange these sizes of ready-made clothes in increasing order.

A: XL
B: S
C: L
D: M

17

Starting with the earliest, arrange these Test cricketers in the order in which they captained India.

A: M S Dhoni
B: Lala Amarnath
C: Mohammed Azharuddin
D: Polly Umrigar

18

Arrange these animals in increasing order of their average body weight.

A: Hippopotamus
B: Alsatian Dog
C: Lion
D: African Elephant

19

Arrange these South Asian countries in ascending order of their population.

A: Nepal
B: Bhutan
C: India
D: Pakistan

20

Starting with the earliest, arrange these Delhi landmarks in the order in which they were built.

A: Jama Masjid
B: Bahai Lotus Temple
C: Qutub Minar
D: Rashtrapati Bhavan

Turn to the answer section on page 227 to see if you've earned a place in the hot seat

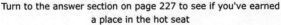

21

Arrange the following actors in the order of their entry into the Hindi film industry.

A: Hema Malini
B: Vidya Balan
C: Sridevi
D: Vyjayanthimala

22

Starting from the north, going south, arrange these languages according to the states in which they are mainly spoken.

A: Konkani
B: Malayalam
C: Punjabi
D: Gujarati

23

Starting with the smallest, arrange these geographical entities in the increasing order of their area and population.

A: Village
B: Town
C: Country
D: State

24

Arrange these historical figures in chronological order.

A: Ashoka
B: Aurangzeb
C: Sher Shah Suri
D: Harshvardhana

25

Arrange these units of time in decreasing order.

A: Year
B: Millennium
C: Decade
D: Century

Turn to the answer section on page 227 to see if you've earned a place in the hot seat

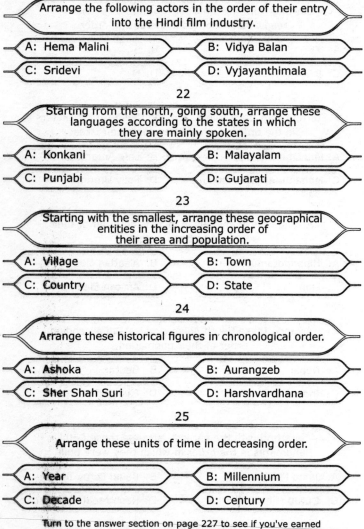

26

Starting with the earliest, arrange these persons in the order in which they first became Union Finance Minister.

A: Pranab Mukherjee
B: Morarji Desai
C: Manmohan Singh
D: P Chidambaram

27

Starting with the least, arrange these groups in ascending order of their number of members.

A: Saptarishi
B: Pandavas
C: Navratnas
D: Kauravas

28

Starting with the smallest, arrange the following islands in increasing order of size.

A: Sri Lanka
B: Greenland
C: Great Britain
D: Singapore

29

Arrange these ruling dynasties in chronological order.

A: Gupta
B: Lodi
C: Maurya
D: Mughal

30

Starting with the earliest, arrange these landmark films in the order in which they were first released.

A: Devdas (Bimal Roy)
B: Alam Ara
C: Sholay
D: Mughal-e-Azam

Turn to the answer section on page 227 to see if you've earned a place in the hot seat

31

Starting from the earliest, arrange these sportspersons in the order in which they first represented India at the Olympics.

A: Leander Paes
B: Abhinav Bindra
C: Dhyan Chand
D: Milkha Singh

32

Starting with the southernmost, arrange these Lok Sabha constituencies from south to north.

A: Jaipur
B: Jabalpur
C: Jalandhar
D: Jammu

33

Arrange these events in Indian history in chronological order.

A: Indo-China War
B: Gandhiji's Assassination
C: Independence
D: 1st General Elections

34

Starting with the youngest, arrange this family of film actors according to seniority.

A: Nutan
B: Tanuja
C: Shobhana Samarth
D: Kajol

35

Starting with the earliest, arrange these warriors in the order in which they commanded the Kaurava army.

A: Karna
B: Dronacharya
C: Bhishma
D: Aswatthama

Turn to the answer section on page 227 to see if you've earned a place in the hot seat

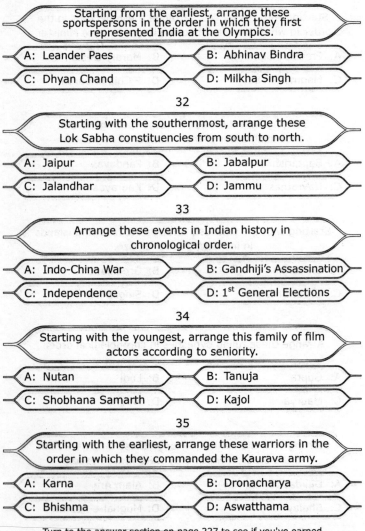

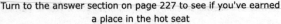

36

Starting with the closest, arrange these cities in increasing order of their distance from the capital of India.

A: Chandigarh
B: Hyderabad
C: Srinagar
D: Chennai

37

Arrange these animals in increasing order of their gestation period.

A: Mouse
B: Man
C: Cat
D: Elephant

38

Starting with the least, arrange these Indian cricketers by the number of Test wickets they have taken.

A: Kapil Dev
B: Sunil Gavaskar
C: Anil Kumble
D: Bishen Singh Bedi

39

Arrange these solid shapes according to the increasing number of flat surfaces they have.

A: Solid Cone
B: Sphere
C: Cube
D: Cylinder

40

Starting from the least, arrange these according to the number of days they have.

A: Week
B: Year
C: Month
D: Fortnight

Turn to the answer section on page 227 to see if you've earned a place in the hot seat

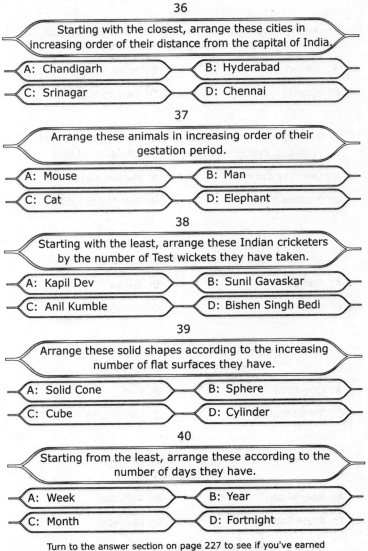

41

Arrange these cities from the nearest to the farthest if you were moving due west from India.

A: Tehran
B: Mumbai
C: Karachi
D: New York City

42

Starting with the shortest, arrange these international sporting events according to their duration of play.

A: One Day Cricket
B: Hockey Match
C: Football Match
D: Test Match Cricket

43

Arrange these geographical entities in the order in which they appear in India's national anthem.

A: Punjab
B: Ganga
C: Gujarat
D: Himachal

44

Starting with the lowest, arrange these fractions in increasing order of their value.

A: One-third
B: Half
C: Three-fourths
D: One-fourth

45

Starting with the earliest, arrange these women rulers in chronological order.

A: Noorjehan
B: Ahilyabai
C: Razia Sultan
D: Laxmibai

Turn to the answer section on page 227 to see if you've earned a place in the hot seat

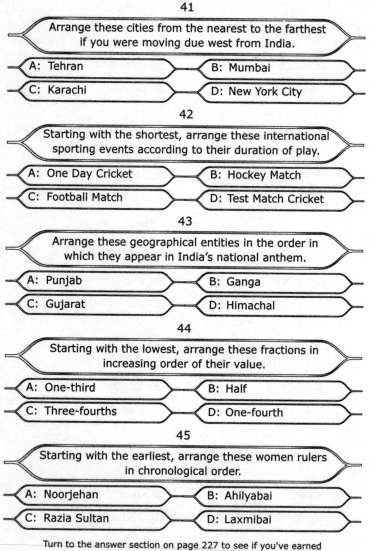

46

Starting with the earliest, arrange these farming activities in order.

A: Harvesting
B: Ploughing
C: Weeding
D: Seeding

47

Starting with the shortest, arrange these in order of their increasing average life span.

A: Dog
B: Elephant
C: Housefly
D: Tortoise

48

Arrange the following holy places from east to west.

A: Mecca
B: Amritsar
C: Dwarka
D: Varanasi

49

Starting from the front and moving backwards, arrange these parts of a car in order.

A: Brake Lights
B: Bonnet
C: Steering Wheel
D: Headlights

50

Starting with the lowest, arrange these cities according to their altitude above mean sea level.

A: Darjeeling
B: Mumbai
C: Delhi
D: Dehradun

Turn to the answer section on page 227 to see if you've earned a place in the hot seat

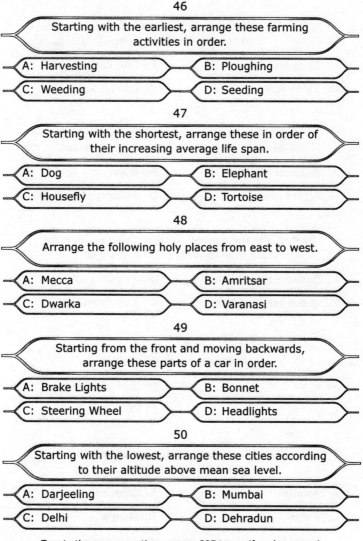

51

Starting with the earliest, arrange these periods in the history of humanity.

A: Computer Age
B: Iron Age
C: Stone Age
D: Bronze Age

52

Starting with the earliest, arrange these film villains in the order in which their first film was released.

A: Ashutosh Rana
B: Pran
C: Amjad Khan
D: Sadashiv Amrapurkar

53

Starting with the earliest, arrange these rulers in the order in which they ruled over Delhi.

A: Bahadur Shah Zafar
B: Ibrahim Lodi
C: Qutub-ud-din Aibak
D: Sher Shah Suri

54

Starting from the smallest, arrange these numbers in increasing order of their value.

A: 0
B: 7
C: 2
D: -7

55

Starting with the earliest, arrange these months of the Saka calendar in order.

A: Ashwin
B: Shravan
C: Kartik
D: Bhadra

Turn to the answer section on page 227 to see if you've earned a place in the hot seat

56

Starting with the part that moves the slowest, arrange these parts on a clock dial in order of their speed.

A: Hour Hand

B: Date Dial

C: Second Hand

D: Minute Hand

57

Starting with the earliest, arrange these poets in chronological order.

A: Amrita Pritam

B: Mirza Ghalib

C: Rabindranath Tagore

D: Kabir

58

Starting with the topmost, arrange these colours in the order in which they appear in the rainbow.

A: Green

B: Violet

C: Red

D: Yellow

59

Starting from the lowest, arrange these means of transport in the order of their area of operation with respect to sea level.

A: Submarine

B: Space Shuttle

C: Ship

D: Aeroplane

60

Starting with the smallest, arrange these cricket scores in ascending order.

A: Century

B: Duck

C: Fifty

D: Triple Century

Turn to the answer section on page 227 to see if you've earned a place in the hot seat

61

Starting with the earliest, arrange these substances in the order in which they were first used by humans.

A: Plastic
B: Bronze
C: Steel
D: Stone

62

Arrange these historic battlefields from north to south.

A: Panipat
B: Srirangapatnam
C: Srinagar
D: Haldighati

63

Arrange these sports in ascending order of the weight of their ball.

A: Shot Put
B: Table Tennis
C: Cricket
D: Basketball

64

Arrange these events as they occurred in the Ramayana.

A: Jatayu's death
B: Sita's swayamvara
C: Lanka dahan
D: Birth of Luv and Kush

65

Arrange these geometric shapes according to the increasing number of sides.

A: Square
B: Octagon
C: Triangle
D: Heptagon

Turn to the answer section on page 227 to see if you've earned a place in the hot seat

66

Starting with the earliest, arrange these inventions in chronological order.

A: Atom Bomb

B: Steam Engine

C: Internet

D: Telephone

67

Starting with the earliest, arrange these films in the order that they were released.

A: 1942: A Love Story

B: 1947: Earth

C: 3 Idiots

D: Taxi No. 9 2 11

68

Starting with the earliest, arrange these religions in the order in which they took root in India.

A: Buddhism

B: Hinduism

C: Islam

D: Sikhism

69

Arrange these parts of a postal address as they are normally written in India.

A: Addressee

B: Pin Code

C: House Number

D: City

70

Starting from the east, arrange these food preparations according to their country of origin.

A: Biryani

B: Hamburger

C: Chowmein

D: Pizza

Turn to the answer section on page 227 to see if you've earned a place in the hot seat

71

Arrange the following as they would occur during a cricket Test match.

A: Toss

B: Tea Break

C: Lunch Break

D: Stumps

72

Starting with the largest, arrange these objects in the universe in decreasing order of their sizes.

A: Earth

B: Milky Way

C: Moon

D: Sun

73

Starting from the most precious, arrange these metals in descending order of their worth.

A: Silver

B: Platinum

C: Copper

D: Gold

74

Starting with the least populated, arrange these countries according to their population.

A: United States of America

B: China

C: India

D: Japan

75

Starting from the month of April, moving down the year, put the following zodiac signs in order.

A: Libra

B: Pisces

C: Capricorn

D: Gemini

Turn to the answer section on page 227 to see if you've earned a place in the hot seat

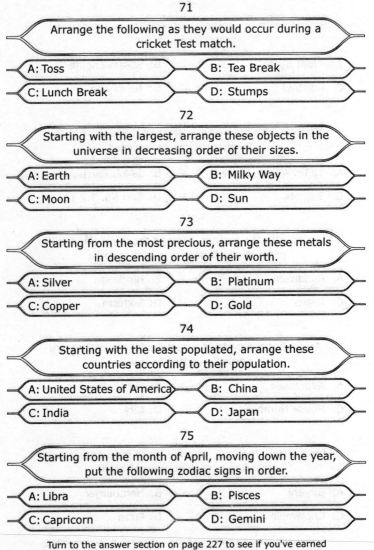

76

Starting with the lowest, arrange these sports in order of increasing distance from the top of the net to the playing surface.

A: Volleyball
B: Table Tennis
C: Lawn Tennis
D: Basketball

77

Arrange the following according to the number of children they have, in descending order.

A: Rabri Devi
B: Maneka Gandhi
C: Sharmila Tagore
D: Hema Malini

78

Starting with the earliest, arrange these occasions in the order in which they are observed in the year.

A: Christmas
B: Independence Day
C: Gandhi Jayanti
D: Republic Day

79

Arrange these cities in the order in which they see the sunrise.

A: Mumbai
B: New York
C: Tokyo
D: London

80

Arrange these in the order in which they are normally worn from head to foot.

A: Nath
B: Choker
C: Tika
D: Payal

Turn to the answer section on page 227 to see if you've earned a place in the hot seat

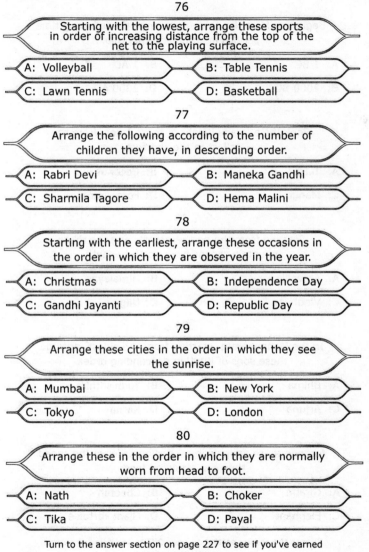

81

Beginning from the earliest, arrange the following time periods in chronological order.

A: 1 BC
B: 1 AD
C: 2000 BC
D: 2000 AD

82

Rank the average height of these trees, from the tallest to the shortest.

A: Tulsi
B: Coconut
C: Mango
D: Pomegranate

83

Starting from the northernmost, arrange these mountain ranges from north to south.

A: Aravallis
B: Himalayas
C: Vindhyas
D: Nilgiris

84

In the Mahabharata, starting from the eldest, arrange these sons of Kunti in descending order.

A: Bhima
B: Yudhishthira
C: Arjuna
D: Karna

85

Arrange these animals in ascending order of the speed they can attain on land.

A: Giraffe
B: Cheetah
C: Elephant
D: Giant Tortoise

Turn to the answer section on page 227 to see if you've earned a place in the hot seat

86

Starting with the earliest, arrange these films of Raj Kapoor in order.

A: Awara

B: Bobby

C: Mera Naam Joker

D: Satyam Shivam Sundaram

87

Starting with the oldest, arrange these Indian political parties in order of their formation.

A: Bharatiya Janata Party

B: CPI

C: Indian National Congress

D: Samajwadi Party

88

Starting from the northernmost, arrange these monuments from north to south.

A: Vivekananda Rock Memorial

B: India Gate

C: Gateway of India

D: Golden Temple

89

Starting from the lowest, arrange these musical notes in ascending order.

A: Re

B: Ni

C: Dha

D: Ma

90

Starting with the earliest, arrange these stages of life, according to Indian tradition, in order.

A: Grihastha

B: Vanaprastha

C: Brahmacharya

D: Sannyasa

Turn to the answer section on page 227 to see if you've earned a place in the hot seat

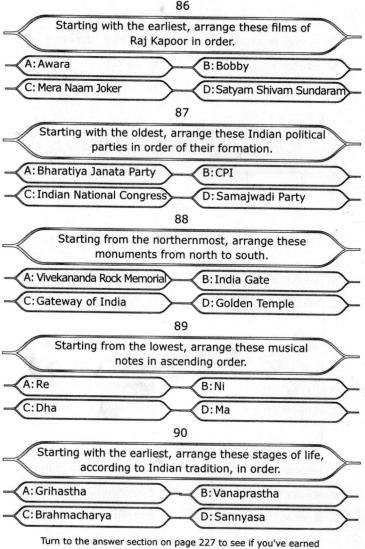

91

Arrange these cities in the order in which they first hosted the Summer Olympic Games.

A: Athens
B: Beijing
C: Atlanta
D: Seoul

92

Starting with the cheapest, arrange these edibles according to their usual prices in India.

A: Sugar
B: Salt
C: Saffron
D: Cashewnut

93

Starting with the earliest, arrange these books in the order that they were published.

A: The God of Small Things
B: Geetanjali
C: Midnight's Children
D: Discovery of India

94

Starting with the youngest, arrange these members of the Kapoor family in order of seniority.

A: Raj Kapoor
B: Shammi Kapoor
C: Shashi Kapoor
D: Prithviraj Kapoor

95

Starting with the earliest, arrange these British personalities in the order in which they came to India.

A: Prince Charles
B: Robert Clive
C: Lord Mountbatten
D: Lord Dalhousie

Turn to the answer section on page 227 to see if you've earned a place in the hot seat

96

Starting with the least, arrange these animals according to the number of legs that they have.

A: Ant
B: Man
C: Centipede
D: Elephant

97

Arrange these television series in the order in which they were first telecast.

A: Jassi Jaissi Koi Nahin
B: Hum Log
C: Buniyaad
D: Fauji

98

Arrange these cities according to the increasing numeric value of their STD codes.

A: Kolkata
B: Mumbai
C: Delhi
D: Chennai

99

Moving down from the head, arrange these beauty treatments in the correct order.

A: Pedicure
B: Perm
C: Manicure
D: Facial

100

Starting with the heaviest, arrange these boxing categories in descending order.

A: Flyweight
B: Heavyweight
C: Middleweight
D: Super Heavyweight

Turn to the answer section on page 227 to see if you've earned a place in the hot seat

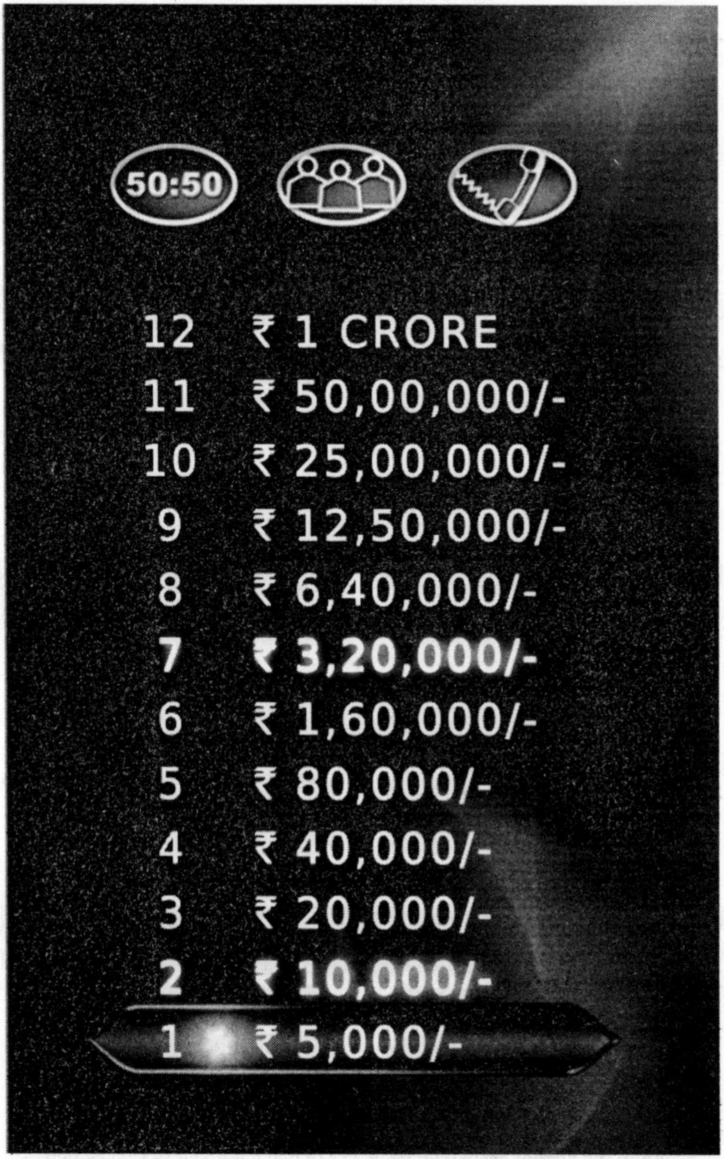
50:50
12 ₹ 1 CRORE
11 ₹ 50,00,000/-
10 ₹ 25,00,000/-
9 ₹ 12,50,000/-
8 ₹ 6,40,000/-
7 ₹ 3,20,000/-
6 ₹ 1,60,000/-
5 ₹ 80,000/-
4 ₹ 40,000/-
3 ₹ 20,000/-
2 ₹ 10,000/-
1 ₹ 5,000/-

1 ♦ ₹5,000

1

In the Raj Kapoor song 'Mera Joota hai Japani...' where is his patloon from?

A: England
B: India
C: Japan
D: Russia

2

Which of these medals is not awarded to competitors at the Olympic Games?

A: Gold
B: Silver
C: Platinum
D: Bronze

3

Which of these is a computer operating system?

A: Doors
B: Portico
C: Gates
D: Windows

4

Which of the following pairs of film stars are not brothers?

A: Salman-Arbaaz
B: Sunny-Bobby
C: Anil-Sanjay
D: Aamir-Fardeen

5

Which of these fruits has more than one seed?

A: Mango
B: Date
C: Guava
D: Litchi

If you would like to use your 50:50 please turn to page 203
If you would like to Ask The Audience please turn to page 215
Turn to the answer section on page 227 to find out if you've won ₹5,000

6

Which is the only planet in our Solar System known to have life on it?

A: Mars
B: Earth
C: Venus
D: Saturn

7

Which of these months has 31 days?

A: March
B: February
C: April
D: September

8

Which God was adoringly called 'Maakhan Chor' as a child?

A: Krishna
B: Kama
C: Ganesha
D: Surya

9

On a cricket scorecard, what does 'c & b' stand for?

A: Caught and Beaten
B: Crawl and Bounce
C: Cow and Bull
D: Caught and Bowled

10

What do the letters 'Ltd.' in a company's name stand for?

A: Label
B: Locked
C: Limited
D: Looted

If you would like to use your 50:50 please turn to page 203
If you would like to Ask The Audience please turn to page 215
Turn to the answer section on page 227 to find out if you've won ₹5,000

11

Normally, what is the colour of the stripes of a zebra crossing?

A: Red
B: Grey
C: White
D: Orange

12

In an Internet address, what does a circle around the letter 'a' mean?

A: Always
B: Access
C: At
D: Almost

13

Who is your paternal grandfather's daughter-in-law?

A: Your Sister
B: Your Daughter
C: Your Niece
D: Your Mother

14

Alphonso is a variety of which fruit?

A: Mango
B: Apple
C: Banana
D: Pineapple

15

Which of these is not a number?

A: Million
B: Trillion
C: Pillion
D: Billion

If you would like to use your 50:50 please turn to page 203
If you would like to Ask The Audience please turn to page 215
Turn to the answer section on page 227 to find out if you've won ₹5,000

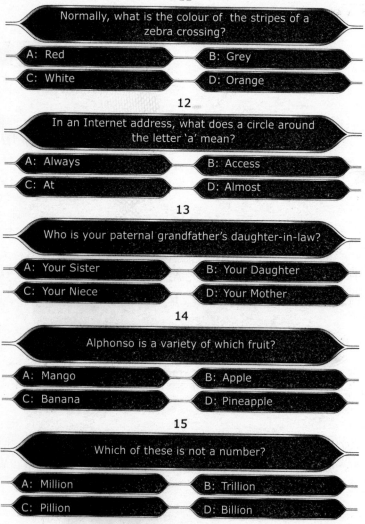

16

Which colour would you get if you mix blue with red?

A: Yellow
B: Green
C: Purple
D: Black

17

Which of these do not have any teeth?

A: Lions
B: Turtles
C: Rats
D: Horses

18

Which of these geometric figures is 3-dimensional?

A: Triangle
B: Circle
C: Square
D: Cube

19

Issuing a 'blank cheque' essentially means which part is to be left blank?

A: Cheque Number
B: Amount of Money
C: Signature
D: Account Number

20

Normally, people of which community use the greeting 'Sat Sri Akal'?

A: Muslim
B: Sikh
C: Buddhist
D: Jain

If you would like to use your 50:50 please turn to page 203
If you would like to Ask The Audience please turn to page 215
Turn to the answer section on page 227 to find out if you've won ₹5,000

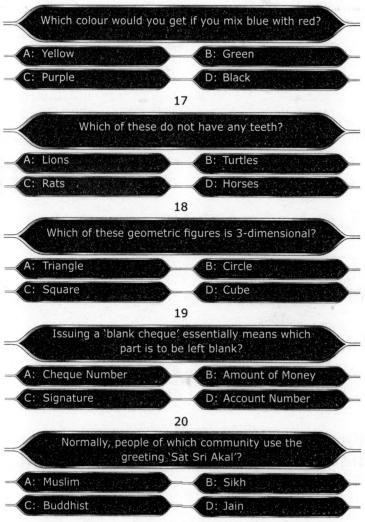

21

Excluding the jokers, how many playing cards does a standard pack have?

A: 51
B: 54
C: 53
D: 52

22

In black coffee, which of these ingredients would be missing?

A: Coffee
B: Sugar
C: Milk
D: Water

23

In which of these would you look up the meaning of a word?

A: Atlas
B: Dictionary
C: Diary
D: Directory

24

What do the letters 'HB' on a pencil stand for?

A: Hard Bound
B: Hard Black
C: Hot Burnt
D: Hand Block

25

Which of the following would best describe a 'jhumka'?

A: An elephant walk
B: A drunken man
C: A dance
D: An earring

If you would like to use your 50:50 please turn to page 203
If you would like to Ask The Audience please turn to page 215
Turn to the answer section on page 228 to find out if you've won ₹5,000

26

During takeoff, aircraft passengers are required to do which of these?

A: Smoke cigarettes
B: Fasten seat belts
C: Walk around
D: Use cell phones

27

If a cycle worth ₹ 1,000 is sold at 50% profit, how much was it sold for?

A: ₹ 1,500
B: ₹ 2,000
C: ₹ 5,000
D: ₹ 10,000

28

Which of these edible items is not the leaf of a plant?

A: Tea
B: Coffee
C: Spinach
D: Lettuce

29

In the Ramayana, who abducted Sita?

A: Kumbhakarna
B: Mareech
C: Ravana
D: Indrajit

30

To signal which of these would a cricket umpire use both his hands?

A: Wide Ball
B: No Ball
C: Out
D: Four Runs

If you would like to use your 50:50 please turn to page 203
If you would like to Ask The Audience please turn to page 215
Turn to the answer section on page 228 to find out if you've won ₹5,000

31

Which of the following terms is not related to computers?

A: Byte
B: Cookie
C: Chip
D: Pastry

32

Which of these is not a variety of 'dal'?

A: Masoor
B: Urad
C: Arhar
D: Zebu

33

If Christmas Day is on a Saturday, on which day would the New Year begin?

A: Saturday
B: Monday
C: Sunday
D: Tuesday

34

Which of these Olympic events is not played across a net?

A: Badminton
B: Table Tennis
C: Fencing
D: Tennis

35

Which of these books is a collection of maps?

A: Atlas
B: Dictionary
C: Thesaurus
D: Bible

If you would like to use your 50:50 please turn to page 203
If you would like to Ask The Audience please turn to page 215
Turn to the answer section on page 228 to find out if you've won ₹5,000

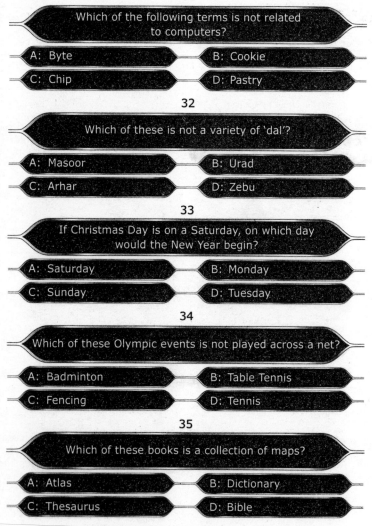

36

What is the numeric value of a right angle?

A: 45 degrees
B: 360 degrees
C: 90 degrees
D: 180 degrees

37

A greenhouse is used to protect which of these?

A: Babies
B: Plants
C: Lions
D: Medicines

38

What is 14th February celebrated as every year?

A: Father's Day
B: Valentine's Day
C: Teachers' Day
D: Children's Day

39

Which of these vehicles would normally have six wheels?

A: Car
B: Bicycle
C: Motorbike
D: Truck

40

How many stumps are used on the pitch in a game of cricket?

A: Four
B: Eight
C: Six
D: Three

If you would like to use your 50:50 please turn to page 203
If you would like to Ask The Audience please turn to page 215
Turn to the answer section on page 228 to find out if you've won ₹5,000

41

What is the profession of the fictional character James Bond?

A: Cricketer
B: Author
C: Politician
D: Secret Agent

42

With which of the following would you associate the term 'Dum Pukht'?

A: Wrestling
B: Medicine
C: Weaving
D: Cooking

43

Which sport is Pete Sampras associated with professionally?

A: Golf
B: Tennis
C: Hockey
D: Boxing

44

In the Oscar-winning film 'Titanic', what was the Titanic?

A: A whale
B: An iceberg
C: A ship
D: A music band

45

Which city is the destination of a letter with the PIN code 400 001?

A: Kolkata
B: New Delhi
C: Mumbai
D: Chennai

If you would like to use your 50:50 please turn to page 203
If you would like to Ask The Audience please turn to page 215
Turn to the answer section on page 228 to find out if you've won ₹5,000

46

Who among these is allowed to carry a walkie-talkie during a cricket match?

A: Captain
B: Wicket-keeper
C: Umpire
D: Third Man

47

With which incarnation of Vishnu do we associate Radha?

A: Vamana
B: Krishna
C: Kalki
D: Matsya

48

If you read 12 pages a day, how long will it take to read a 96 page book?

A: Eight
B: Five
C: Seven
D: Six

49

Which of these is not an ape?

A: Gorilla
B: Chimpanzee
C: Orangutan
D: Monkey

50

Which two colours are usually represented on a chess board?

A: Black & Blue
B: Red & White
C: Green & Yellow
D: Black & White

If you would like to use your 50:50 please turn to page 203
If you would like to Ask The Audience please turn to page 215
Turn to the answer section on page 228 to find out if you've won ₹5,000

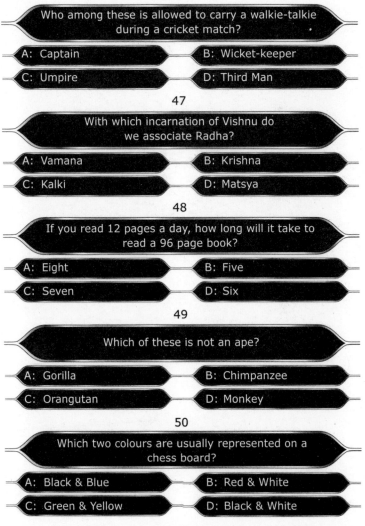

51

By what other name is the Indian national flag also known?

A: Satranga
B: Chauranga
C: Nauranga
D: Tiranga

52

How many runs should a bowler concede in an over to qualify it as a maiden?

A: Six
B: Thirty-six
C: Zero
D: One

53

Which of these is a machine through which one can withdraw cash?

A: ATP
B: ATE
C: ATC
D: ATM

54

Which of these lenses touches the eyeball?

A: Binocular Lens
B: Spectacle Lens
C: Contact Lens
D: Telescope Lens

55

Which of these shapes has only four corners?

A: Pentagon
B: Triangle
C: Circle
D: Rectangle

If you would like to use your 50:50 please turn to page 203
If you would like to Ask The Audience please turn to page 215
Turn to the answer section on page 228 to find out if you've won ₹5,000

56

Which of these sports is also the name of something that can be drunk?

A: Polo
B: Squash
C: Golf
D: Croquet

57

Which of these days falls exactly nine months after Valentine's Day in India?

A: Independence Day
B: Republic Day
C: Children's Day
D: Teachers' Day

58

Which of these is not a musical duo?

A: Jatin Lalit
B: Nadeem Shravan
C: Anand Milind
D: Ismail Darbar

59

Which Hindu god is often depicted with a peacock feather in his hair?

A: Brahma
B: Kama
C: Kartikeya
D: Krishna

60

With reference to management, who would an 'MD' of a company be?

A: Major Domo
B: Managing Director
C: Most Destructive
D: Male Dominant

If you would like to use your 50:50 please turn to page 203
If you would like to Ask The Audience please turn to page 215
Turn to the answer section on page 228 to find out if you've won ₹5,000

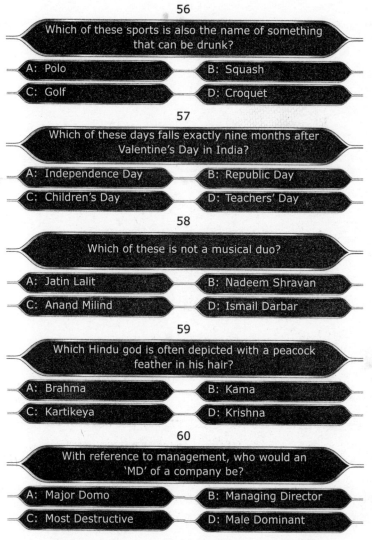

61

Which of these does not feed on nectar?

A: Sparrow
B: Hummingbird
C: Bee
D: Bat

62

What is the shape of a tennis court?

A: Square
B: Rectangular
C: Diamond
D: Circular

63

Which of these films starred both Salman Khan and Aamir Khan in lead roles?

A: Mela
B: Karan Arjun
C: Andaz Apna Apna
D: Hello Brother

64

Which of these cards would one use to buy goods?

A: Postcard
B: Visiting Card
C: Greeting Card
D: Credit Card

65

Which of these is not a state of matter?

A: Solid
B: Time
C: Liquid
D: Gas

If you would like to use your 50:50 please turn to page 203
If you would like to Ask The Audience please turn to page 215
Turn to the answer section on page 228 to find out if you've won ₹5,000

66

On which creatures was the film 'Jurassic Park' based?

A: Dolphins
B: Sharks
C: Dinosaurs
D: Elephants

67

Which of these would you associate with a kind of pen?

A: Lake
B: River
C: Fountain
D: Waterfall

68

Which colour appears at the top of the Indian tricolour?

A: Green
B: White
C: Blue
D: Saffron

69

At what time do the hands of a clock make a straight line vertically across a dial?

A: 12:00
B: 6:00
C: 9:15
D: 3:45

70

In which of these sports does each team not have 11 players?

A: Football
B: Hockey
C: Basketball
D: Cricket

If you would like to use your 50:50 please turn to page 203
If you would like to Ask The Audience please turn to page 215
Turn to the answer section on page 228 to find out if you've won ₹5,000

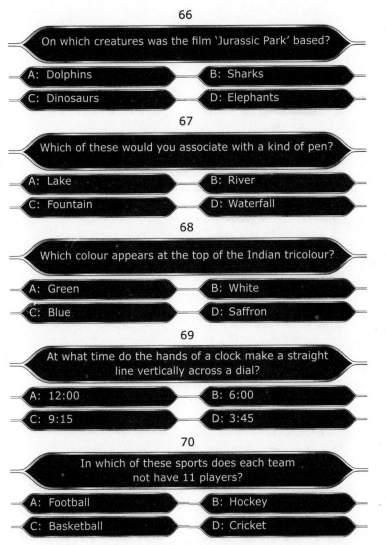

71

In which city in India is the Lotus temple of the Ba'hai's located?

A: New Delhi
B: Mumbai
C: Indore
D: Gwalior

72

What is Kung Fu?

A: A Korean city
B: A martial art
C: A Chinese dish
D: A Thai soup

73

Which of the following would best describe a website?

A: Spider's home
B: Internet site
C: Holiday home
D: Duck's foot

74

Which of these fictional characters had a magic lamp?

A: Ali Baba
B: Sindbad
C: Aladdin
D: Simsim

75

How many months in a year have 31 days?

A: Seven
B: Six
C: Five
D: Four

If you would like to use your 50:50 please turn to page 204
If you would like to Ask The Audience please turn to page 216
Turn to the answer section on page 228 to find out if you've won ₹5,000

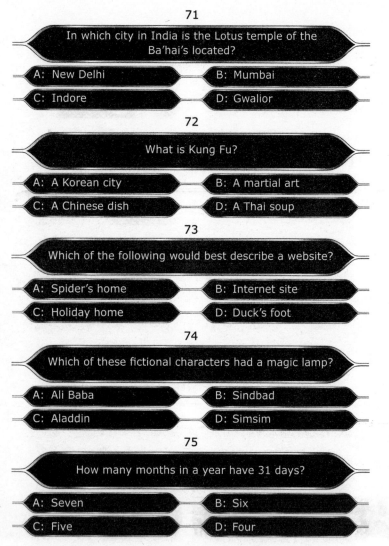

76

Which of these would you require to visit a foreign country?

A: Password | B: Passbook
C: Passover | D: Passport

77

From which of these is ketchup normally made?

A: Apple | B: Orange
C: Tomato | D: Strawberry

78

What does a cricket umpire signal by extending one arm horizontally?

A: Leg Bye | B: Wide
C: No Ball | D: Out

79

In Walt Disney's cartoons, what kind of an animal is Mickey?

A: Mouse | B: Dog
C: Duck | D: Cat

80

Which of these members of a cricket team may not bowl in a match?

A: Captain | B: Vice Captain
C: Substitute | D: Wicket-keeper

If you would like to use your 50:50 please turn to page 204
If you would like to Ask The Audience please turn to page 216
Turn to the answer section on page 228 to find out if you've won ₹5,000

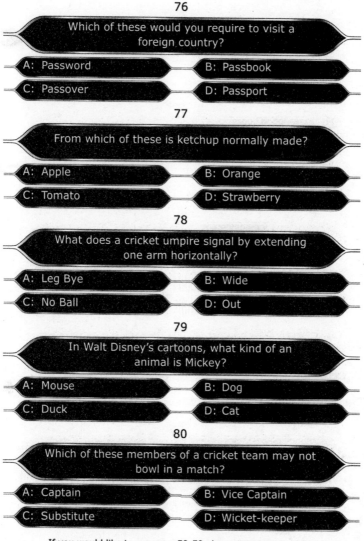

81

What surname is common to film actresses Geeta, Yogita and Vyjayanthimala?

A: Kapoor
B: Dutt
C: Kumari
D: Bali

82

A bronze medal is usually awarded as which of these prizes?

A: First
B: Second
C: Third
D: Fourth

83

Which part of a cabbage is usually eaten in salads?

A: Seeds
B: Roots
C: Stem
D: Leaves

84

The nickname of which Bollywood actress is 'Bebo'?

A: Kajol
B: Juhi Chawla
C: Kareena Kapoor
D: Karisma Kapoor

85

What is the square root of 100?

A: One
B: Ten
C: Eight
D: Five

If you would like to use your 50:50 please turn to page 204
If you would like to Ask The Audience please turn to page 216
Turn to the answer section on page 228 to find out if you've won ₹5,000

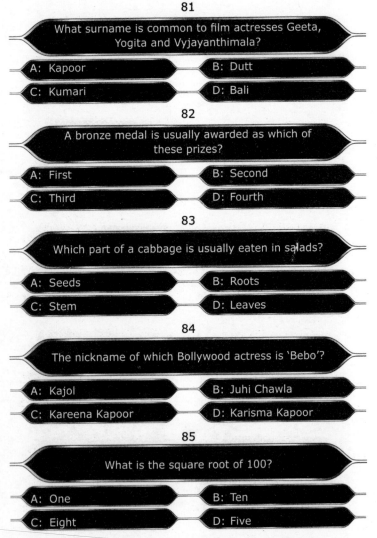

86

How many bags of wool does the nursery rhyme 'Baa baa black sheep' mention?

A: Four
B: Two
C: Three
D: Five

87

Which Indian musician was also popularly known as 'Pancham' ?

A: C Ramachandran
B: S D Burman
C: R D Burman
D: Ravindra Jain

88

Which of these cards is not present in a standard pack of playing cards?

A: King
B: Queen
C: Jack
D: Jill

89

Which is the shortest month in a leap year?

A: January
B: February
C: September
D: April

90

In which of these sports would you use a bat?

A: Basketball
B: Baseball
C: Netball
D: Football

If you would like to use your 50:50 please turn to page 204
If you would like to Ask The Audience please turn to page 216
Turn to the answer section on page 228 to find out if you've won ₹5,000

91

If we square 1, what do we get?

A: 0
B: 4
C: 2
D: 1

92

How many sides does a parallelogram have?

A: Four
B: Three
C: Six
D: Two

93

With which number would you associate the fictional character James Bond?

A: 747
B: 303
C: 420
D: 007

94

Which of these sports does not use a spherical ball?

A: Billiards
B: Rugby
C: Table Tennis
D: Squash

95

Which of these animals' bite does not cause rabies?

A: Dog
B: Fox
C: Snake
D: Bat

If you would like to use your 50:50 please turn to page 204
If you would like to Ask The Audience please turn to page 216
Turn to the answer section on page 228 to find out if you've won ₹5,000

96

In the Ramayana, how many heads did Ravana have?

A: Eight
B: Ten
C: Twelve
D: Fourteen

97

In which city would you find the temple of Mumba Devi?

A: Mysore
B: Mumbai
C: Manipal
D: Mahabaleshwar

98

Which of these does not have wings?

A: Aeroplane
B: Butterfly
C: Duck
D: Parachute

99

Who among the following is a daughter of actor Raj Kapoor?

A: Krishna
B: Karisma
C: Kareena
D: Rima

100

Who would normally wear diapers?

A: Batsmen
B: Models
C: Babies
D: Dogs

If you would like to use your 50:50 please turn to page 204
If you would like to Ask The Audience please turn to page 216
Turn to the answer section on page 228 to find out if you've won ₹5,000

101

Which of these is a unit of length?

A: cc
B: MB
C: cm
D: GB

102

Pekoe and dust are types of which of these?

A: Coffee
B: Tea
C: Sugar
D: Rice

103

Which of these mathematical expressions is not true?

A: 4 x 2 = 2 x 4
B: 4 + 2 = 2 + 4
C: 4 - 2 = 2 - 4
D: 4 = 2 x 2

104

Which of these does not use a flame to give light?

A: Bonfire
B: Candle
C: Match
D: Light Bulb

105

In which of these sports can a maximum of two players play at a time?

A: Tennis
B: Boxing
C: Polo
D: Table Tennis

If you would like to use your 50:50 please turn to page 204
If you would like to Ask The Audience please turn to page 216
Turn to the answer section on page 228 to find out if you've won ₹5,000

106

Which of these items of stationery does not make holes in paper when used?

A: Stapler
B: Punch
C: Paper Clip
D: Pin

107

Which of the following would best describe 'headlines'?

A: Forehead Wrinkles
B: Main Sea Routes
C: Main News Items
D: Main Rail Routes

108

What is a mainframe?

A: Space Shuttle
B: Large Computer
C: Radio Station
D: Video Game

109

How many days are there in 7 weeks?

A: Seventy
B: Forty-nine
C: Fifty
D: Thirty-one

110

Which of the following will you find on a pressure cooker?

A: Safety Pin
B: Safety Jacket
C: Safety Valve
D: Safety Belt

If you would like to use your 50:50 please turn to page 204
If you would like to Ask The Audience please turn to page 216
Turn to the answer section on page 228 to find out if you've won ₹5,000

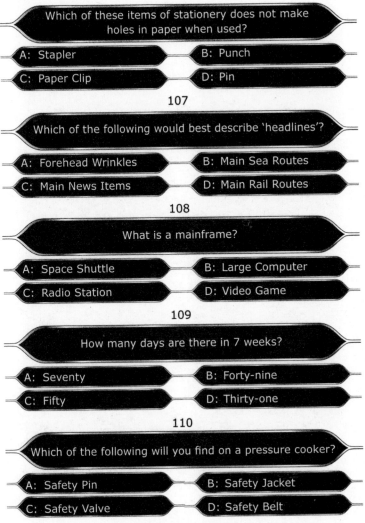

111

Which precious stone is said to be 'a woman's best friend'?

A: Ruby
B: Diamond
C: Pearl
D: Topaz

112

If you stand facing the rising sun, what is the direction to your left?

A: East
B: West
C: North
D: South

113

If tandoori roti is thick, which roti is very thin?

A: Naan
B: Paratha
C: Rumali
D: Kulcha

114

How many millimetres are there in a metre?

A: 10
B: 100
C: 1,000
D: 10,000

115

With reference to cricket, what does the 'L' in 'LBW' stand for?

A: Low
B: Leg
C: Line
D: Leap

If you would like to use your 50:50 please turn to page 204
If you would like to Ask The Audience please turn to page 216
Turn to the answer section on page 228 to find out if you've won ₹5,000

116

Which of these ingredients in a curry would give it a yellow colour?

A: Elaichi
B: Ajwain
C: Dhaniya
D: Haldi

117

How many days are there in a leap year?

A: 365
B: 366
C: 364
D: 367

118

In which of these cities could you spend an evening at a beach?

A: Cherrapunji
B: Chittor
C: Chennai
D: Chandigarh

119

Coins of which of these denominations is not found in the Indian currency?

A: ₹ 1
B: ₹ 5
C: ₹ 2
D: ₹ 15

120

How would seawater normally taste?

A: Sour
B: Salty
C: Tasteless
D: Bitter

If you would like to use your 50:50 please turn to page 204
If you would like to Ask The Audience please turn to page 216
Turn to the answer section on page 228 to find out if you've won ₹5,000

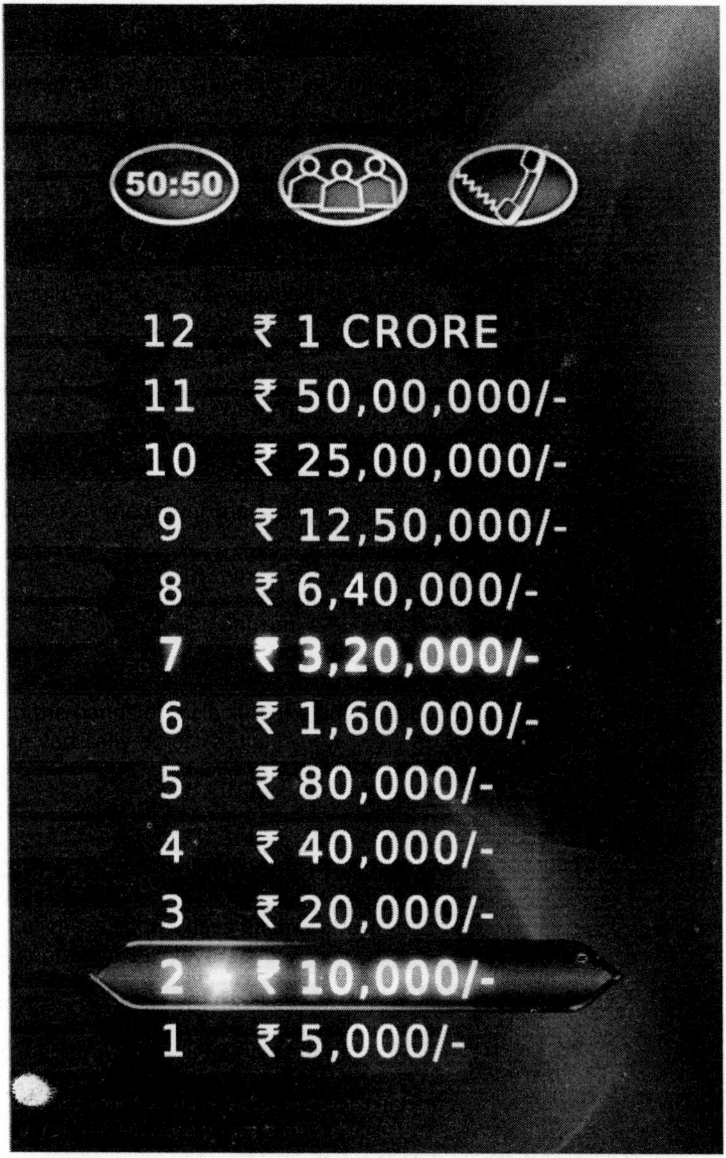
50:50
12 ₹ 1 CRORE
11 ₹ 50,00,000/-
10 ₹ 25,00,000/-
9 ₹ 12,50,000/-
8 ₹ 6,40,000/-
7 ₹ 3,20,000/-
6 ₹ 1,60,000/-
5 ₹ 80,000/-
4 ₹ 40,000/-
3 ₹ 20,000/-
2 ₹ 10,000/-
1 ₹ 5,000/-

2 ✦ ₹10,000

1

In which year will India observe the bicentenary of its Independence?

A: 2047
B: 2147
C: 2247
D: 2097

2

Which Hindi film actor is married to Dr Sriram Nene?

A: Poonam Dhillon
B: Kajol
C: Madhuri Dixit
D: Tina Munim

3

Which river flows through the capital of India?

A: Ganga
B: Yamuna
C: Sabarmati
D: Narmada

4

What is the minimum number of people required to form a Panchayat?

A: Three
B: Six
C: Seven
D: Five

5

Which of these instruments is used to view distant objects?

A: Barometer
B: Binoculars
C: Microscope
D: Stethoscope

If you would like to use your 50:50 please turn to page 204
If you would like to Ask The Audience please turn to page 216
Turn to the answer section on page 228 to find out if you've won ₹10,000

6

How many minutes are there in a day?

A: 1,440
B: 1,480
C: 1,880
D: 1,240

7

Which of these terms refers to a delivery in cricket?

A: Leg Puller
B: Leg Cutter
C: Leg Chopper
D: Leg Grinder

8

What would distinguish even an identical twin from its sibling?

A: Hair
B: Fingerprints
C: Finger Nails
D: Eye Colour

9

The purity of which of these is normally measured in carats or karats?

A: Aluminium
B: Bronze
C: Gold
D: Iron

10

Which of these is not a wind instrument?

A: Saxophone
B: Trumpet
C: Flute
D: Violin

If you would like to use your 50:50 please turn to page 204
If you would like to Ask The Audience please turn to page 216
Turn to the answer section on page 228 to find out if you've won ₹10,000

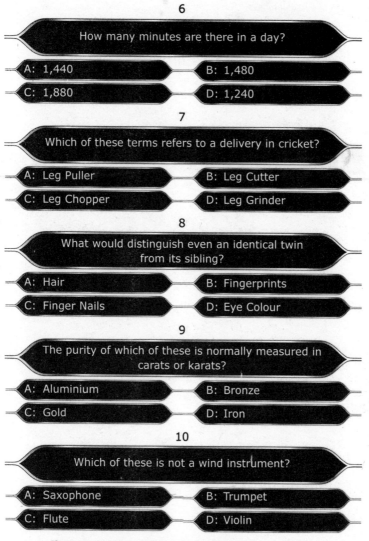

11

Which of these Hindi films does not feature the actor Govinda?

A: Coolie No.1

B: Hero No.1

C: Biwi No.1

D: Aunty No.1

12

Which of these is a character from 'The Thousand and One Nights'?

A: Aladdin

B: Othello

C: Baba Yaga

D: Tintin

13

The Sanchi Stupa is a place of pilgrimage for which religious community?

A: Sikhs

B: Buddhists

C: Christians

D: Muslims

14

What is your height in inches if you are six feet tall?

A: Sixty

B: Seventy-two

C: Seventy

D: Eighty-four

15

Which of the following is not present on the Moon?

A: Gravity

B: Craters

C: Plants

D: Mountains

If you would like to use your 50:50 please turn to page 204
If you would like to Ask The Audience please turn to page 216
Turn to the answer section on page 228 to find out if you've won ₹10,000

16

How many arms does an octopus have?

A: Ten
B: Nine
C: Eight
D: Four

17

Which animal is often referred to as 'man's best friend'?

A: Cat
B: Monkey
C: Donkey
D: Dog

18

How many 25 paise coins constitute five rupees?

A: Twenty
B: Twenty-five
C: Forty
D: Ten

19

Which part of a coffee plant is used to prepare the beverage?

A: Leaves
B: Beans
C: Bark
D: Roots

20

How is Neetu Singh related to Kareena Kapoor?

A: Mausi
B: Tai
C: Chachi
D: Bua

If you would like to use your 50:50 please turn to page 204
If you would like to Ask The Audience please turn to page 216
Turn to the answer section on page 228 to find out if you've won ₹10,000

21

Which of these birds is mentioned in the song 'Saare jahan se acchha...'?

A: Koel | B: Bulbul
C: Mynah | D: Tota

22

In which of these sports do the opponents not play standing face-to-face?

A: Table Tennis | B: Badminton
C: Tennis | D: Squash

23

Which of these would normally float on water?

A: Ink | B: Petrol
C: Sand | D: Chalk

24

Which part of the carrot plant do we usually eat?

A: Stem | B: Fruit
C: Root | D: Branch

25

Traditionally, on which flower is Goddess Lakshmi represented as standing?

A: Rose | B: Marigold
C: Lotus | D: Sunflower

If you would like to use your 50:50 please turn to page 204
If you would like to Ask The Audience please turn to page 216
Turn to the answer section on page 228 to find out if you've won ₹10,000

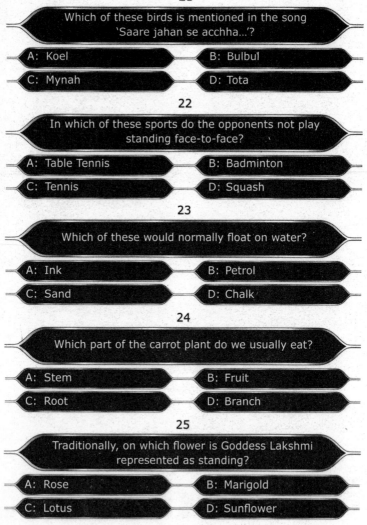

26

What is a protractor used to measure?

A: Radiation
B: Humidity
C: Intensity of Fog
D: Angles

27

Which was the first day of the 20th century?

A: 1 January 1901
B: 1 January 1801
C: 1 January 1701
D: 1 January 2001

28

In a car with manual transmission, what should one press to change gears?

A: Clutch
B: Brake
C: Accelerator
D: Handbrake

29

Which fruit is dried to make raisin or 'kishmish'?

A: Figs
B: Dates
C: Berries
D: Grapes

30

What is the maximum number of wickets that a team can lose in a Test match?

A: Ten
B: Eleven
C: Twenty
D: Twenty-two

If you would like to use your 50:50 please turn to page 204
If you would like to Ask The Audience please turn to page 216
Turn to the answer section on page 228 to find out if you've won ₹10,000

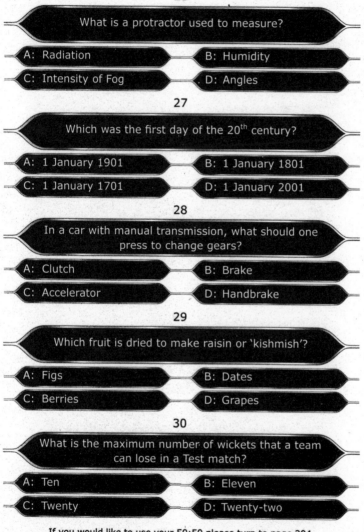

31

Which colour is common to the flags of India and Bangladesh?

A: Green
B: White
C: Blue
D: Saffron

32

How many black pawns are there at the beginning of a game of chess?

A: Four
B: Six
C: Eight
D: Sixteen

33

Which of these is not a metric unit?

A: Decametre
B: Millimetre
C: Minimetre
D: Decimetre

34

Which of these is not a medicinal drug?

A: Aspirin
B: Tarpaulin
C: Disprin
D: Streptomycin

35

In the Ramayana, who burnt Lanka after his tail was set on fire?

A: Sugriva
B: Angada
C: Hanuman
D: Nala

If you would like to use your 50:50 please turn to page 205
If you would like to Ask The Audience please turn to page 217
Turn to the answer section on page 228 to find out if you've won ₹10,000

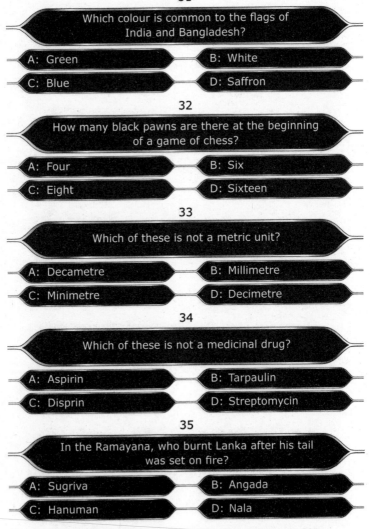

36

Who is believed to come down a chimney with gifts on Christmas Eve?

A: Jesus
B: Mary
C: Santa Claus
D: St. Peter

37

How many minutes are there in between 10:15 a.m. and 11:05 a.m.?

A: 20 minutes
B: 50 minutes
C: 10 minutes
D: 45 minutes

38

Which of these musical instruments is actually a simple clay pot?

A: Mridangam
B: Ghatam
C: Tabla
D: Dholak

39

Which country lies between Bhutan and Bangladesh?

A: Pakistan
B: Nepal
C: India
D: Myanmar

40

Which of these professionals would have needed to complete an LLB course?

A: A Lecturer
B: A Lawyer
C: A Linguist
D: A Librarian

If you would like to use your 50:50 please turn to page 205
If you would like to Ask The Audience please turn to page 217
Turn to the answer section on page 228 to find out if you've won ₹10,000

41

In which of these sports are animals not required?

A: Polo
B: Show Jumping
C: Water Polo
D: Bullfighting

42

How many right angles would a right angled triangle have?

A: One
B: Two
C: None
D: Three

43

What is the chemical symbol for hydrogen?

A: H
B: He
C: Cu
D: Na

44

Which of the following animals changes colour?

A: Snakes
B: Beetles
C: Bees
D: Chameleons

45

In Hindu mythology, whose elder brother was Balrama?

A: Rama
B: Krishna
C: Arjuna
D: Parshurama

If you would like to use your 50:50 please turn to page 205
If you would like to Ask The Audience please turn to page 217
Turn to the answer section on page 228 to find out if you've won ₹10,000

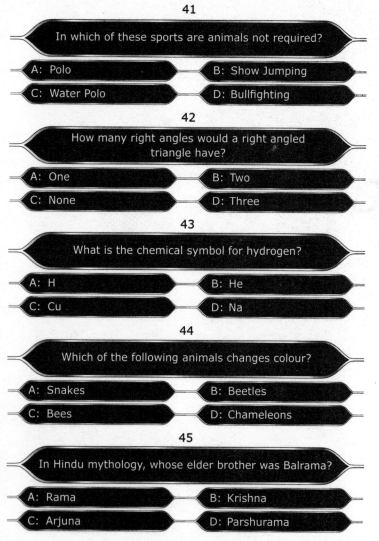

46

Which of these states does not have any port?

A: Orissa
B: Andhra Pradesh
C: West Bengal
D: Chhattisgarh

47

On the bank of which river is the Taj Mahal situated?

A: Ganga
B: Yamuna
C: Gomti
D: Gandak

48

Which of these festivals is also known as Vijayadashami?

A: Diwali
B: Pongal
C: Dussehra
D: Holi

49

Which of these states was carved out of Uttar Pradesh?

A: Uttarakhand
B: Chhattisgarh
C: Jharkhand
D: Vidarbha

50

What angle is fomed by the hour and minute hands of a clock at 3:00 p.m.?

A: 90 degrees
B: 180 degrees
C: 60 degrees
D: 45 degrees

If you would like to use your 50:50 please turn to page 205
If you would like to Ask The Audience please turn to page 217
Turn to the answer section on page 228 to find out if you've won ₹10,000

51

Which of these sports does not require a player to put a ball into a hole?

A: Golf
B: Billiards
C: Snooker
D: Baseball

52

In mathematics, what is a whole number divisible exactly by 2 called?

A: Prime Number
B: Even Number
C: Odd Number
D: Fraction

53

Cinnamon is obtained from which part of the plant?

A: Bark
B: Leaf
C: Flower
D: Root

54

Which of these is not a name for Lord Ganesha?

A: Vinayaka
B: Damodara
C: Lambodara
D: Ganpati

55

Which of these sports is also the name of an insect?

A: Polo
B: Hockey
C: Cricket
D: Squash

If you would like to use your 50:50 please turn to page 205
If you would like to Ask The Audience please turn to page 217
Turn to the answer section on page 228 to find out if you've won ₹10,000

56

Which of these is a pacemaker?

A: Cricket Bowler
B: Clock
C: Steam Engine
D: Heart Stimulator

57

What name is given to the part of an aeroplane where a pilot sits?

A: Pulpit
B: Soakpit
C: Cockpit
D: Pitstop

58

In which continent is the southernmost point of the Earth located?

A: Antarctica
B: South America
C: Australia
D: Arctic

59

On whose samadhi are the words 'Hey Ram' engraved?

A: Jawaharlal Nehru
B: Indira Gandhi
C: Mahatma Gandhi
D: Rajiv Gandhi

60

Which one of these is not a card game?

A: Rummy
B: Ektara
C: Solitaire
D: Bridge

If you would like to use your 50:50 please turn to page 205
If you would like to Ask The Audience please turn to page 217
Turn to the answer section on page 228 to find out if you've won ₹10,000

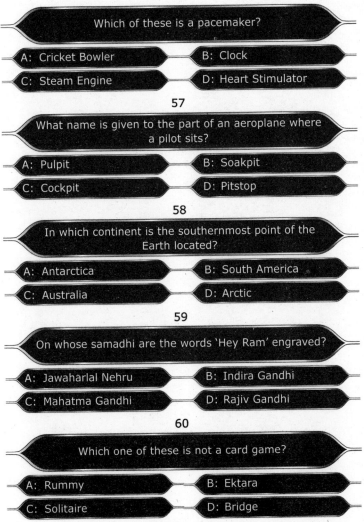

61

In an equilateral triangle, how many sides are of equal length?

A: One
B: Two
C: None
D: All

62

Which of the following animals is a herbivore?

A: Horse
B: Grizzly Bear
C: Cat
D: Seal

63

According to Hindu mythology, whose weapon was the Sudarshan Chakra?

A: Dronacharya
B: Bhishma
C: Arjuna
D: Vishnu

64

Which of these oils is obtained from the fruit and not the seed of a plant?

A: Sunflower Oil
B: Peanut Oil
C: Sesame Oil
D: Olive Oil

65

Which of these fruits is normally used for making wine?

A: Grape
B: Mango
C: Apple
D: Guava

If you would like to use your 50:50 please turn to page 205
If you would like to Ask The Audience please turn to page 217
Turn to the answer section on page 229 to find out if you've won ₹10,000

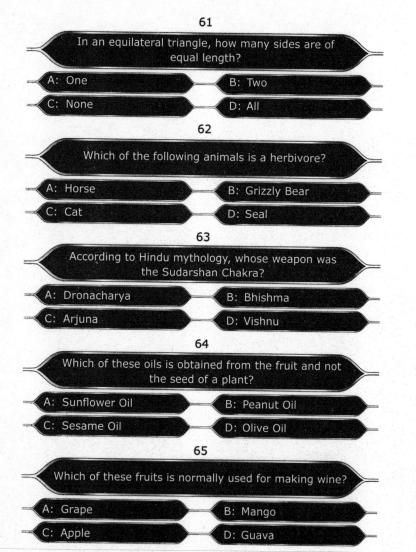

66

The presence of which of these is not needed in a civil marriage?

A: Bride

B: Bridegroom

C: Registrar

D: Priest

67

In which of these would the water normally be stationary?

A: Pond

B: Waterfall

C: River

D: Fountain

68

How many zodiac signs are there?

A: Ten

B: Twelve

C: Fourteen

D: Sixteen

69

In which game would you use bishops, kings and queens?

A: Ludo

B: Rummy

C: Chess

D: Bridge

70

How many planets are there in the Solar System?

A: Nine

B: Twelve

C: Ten

D: Eight

If you would like to use your 50:50 please turn to page 205
If you would like to Ask The Audience please turn to page 217
Turn to the answer section on page 229 to find out if you've won ₹10,000

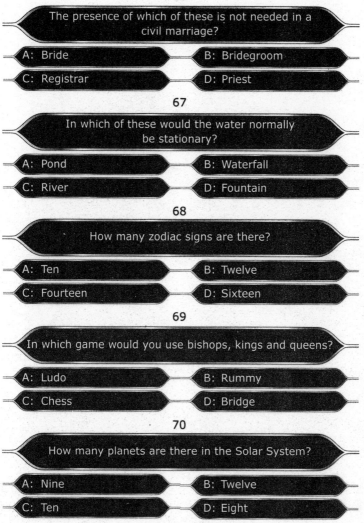

71

Which of these creatures has legs?

A: Earthworm
B: Caterpillar
C: Leech
D: Snake

72

Conjunctivitis affects which part of the body?

A: Nose
B: Ears
C: Eyes
D: Kidney

73

What does the 'C' in VCR stand for?

A: Cassette
B: Compact
C: Cable
D: Cinema

74

Which of these would you not find in a first-aid kit?

A: Band-aid
B: Cottonwool
C: Pacemaker
D: Gauze Bandage

75

Which of these creatures has a sting in its tail?

A: Termite
B: Cockroach
C: Grass Snake
D: Scorpion

If you would like to use your 50:50 please turn to page 205
If you would like to Ask The Audience please turn to page 217
Turn to the answer section on page 229 to find out if you've won ₹10,000

76

'Rabi' and 'Kharif' are terms associated with which of these?

A: Crops
B: Kites
C: Colours
D: Kabaddi

77

In which state of India would you find the fort city of Jaisalmer?

A: Rajasthan
B: Gujarat
C: Uttar Pradesh
D: Madhya Pradesh

78

What is the minimum legal age for marriage for men in India?

A: Eighteen
B: Sixteen
C: Twenty-five
D: Twenty-one

79

How many faces does a standard dice have?

A: Nine
B: Four
C: Six
D: Twelve

80

Which of the following is not a term associated with computers?

A: Internet
B: Cyber
C: GMAT
D: Binary

If you would like to use your 50:50 please turn to page 205
If you would like to Ask The Audience please turn to page 217
Turn to the answer section on page 229 to find out if you've won ₹10,000

81

Which of these plants is not a source of edible oil?

A: Coconut
B: Groundnut
C: Sunflower
D: Rubber

82

How many sense organs does the human body normally have?

A: One
B: Six
C: Four
D: Five

83

Which of these is not associated with the postal department?

A: Money Order
B: Postal Order
C: Demand Draft
D: Speed Post

84

Which of these is not a natural form of water?

A: Iceberg
B: Snow
C: Hailstone
D: Dry Ice

85

Which of these car models is not manufactured by Maruti Udyog Limited?

A: Swift
B: WagonR
C: Ikon
D: Alto

If you would like to use your 50:50 please turn to page 205
If you would like to Ask The Audience please turn to page 217
Turn to the answer section on page 229 to find out if you've won ₹10,000

86

How would 'a x b' be represented in algebra?

A: a+b

B: 2a+2b

C: ab

D: 2(a+b)

87

In which city is the Charminar located?

A: Fatehpur Sikri

B: Hyderabad

C: Udaipur

D: Mysore

88

Which country is personified as 'Uncle Sam'?

A: UK

B: Canada

C: USA

D: Australia

89

A chequered flag of which colours is waved to mark the end of a car race?

A: Black and White

B: Black and Red

C: Red and Blue

D: Red and White

90

What colour would you get if you mixed equal quantities of blue and yellow?

A: Purple

B: Orange

C: Brown

D: Green

If you would like to use your 50:50 please turn to page 205
If you would like to Ask The Audience please turn to page 217
Turn to the answer section on page 229 to find out if you've won ₹10,000

91

How many legs does a spider have?

A: Four
B: Six
C: Eight
D: Twelve

92

In cricket, which of these terms refers to a non-batsman who is batting?

A: Third Man
B: Twelfth Man
C: Nightwatchman
D: Groundsman

93

What are 'bell-bottoms' a type of?

A: Shoes
B: Hats
C: Shirts
D: Trousers

94

In the game of carom, what is the colour of the coin known as the 'queen'?

A: Red
B: Black
C: White
D: Brown

95

Which of these Hindi films did not feature the heroine in a double role?

A: Sharmilee
B: Chalbaaz
C: Aradhana
D: Seeta Aur Geeta

If you would like to use your 50:50 please turn to page 205
If you would like to Ask The Audience please turn to page 217
Turn to the answer section on page 229 to find out if you've won ₹10,000

96

In which of these water bodies are the Lakshadweep Islands located?

A: Arabian Sea
B: Indian Ocean
C: Bay of Bengal
D: Gulf of Kutch

97

Which of the following regions is not named in the Indian National Anthem?

A: Punjab
B: Himachal
C: Gujarat
D: Delhi

98

How many cards of the suit of hearts are there in a standard pack of cards?

A: 12
B: 10
C: 13
D: 20

99

How many degrees are there in a circle?

A: 180 degrees
B: 360 degrees
C: 90 degrees
D: 240 degrees

100

What are Hilsa and Rohu types of?

A: Trees
B: Birds
C: Deer
D: Fish

If you would like to use your 50:50 please turn to page 205
If you would like to Ask The Audience please turn to page 217
Turn to the answer section on page 229 to find out if you've won ₹10,000

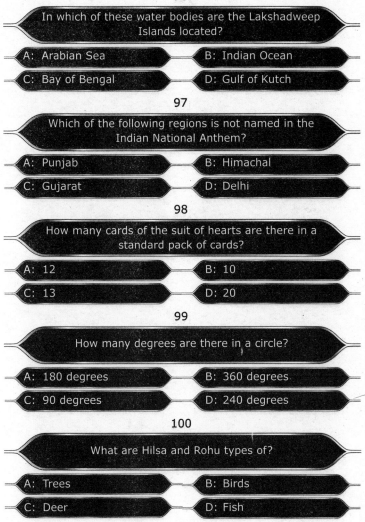

101

Which of these is a fielding position in cricket?

A: Straight Leg | B: Extra Leg
C: Round Leg | D: Square Leg

102

The natural habitat of which of these is not in the polar regions?

A: Penguins | B: Polar Bears
C: Seals | D: Yak

103

Of which word is 'memo' a short form?

A: Memorise | B: Momentum
C: Memorandum | D: Memento

104

Which of these bodily actions cools a dog's body?

A: Wagging its Tail | B: Running
C: Panting | D: Barking

105

Which weekday is named after the only natural satellite of the Earth?

A: Tuesday | B: Thursday
C: Sunday | D: Monday

If you would like to use your 50:50 please turn to page 205
If you would like to Ask The Audience please turn to page 217
Turn to the answer section on page 229 to find out if you've won ₹10,000

106

The Shias and Sunnis are two major sects of which religion?

A: Christianity
B: Judaism
C: Islam
D: Zoroastrianism

107

What numerical value is denoted by one 'score'?

A: Ten
B: Twenty
C: Fifty
D: Twenty-four

108

What is the source of hydroelectric power?

A: Uranium
B: Water
C: Wind
D: Sun

109

Which of these is not a cricket stroke?

A: Cut
B: Glance
C: Hook
D: Putt

110

Which of these birds are trained and used to send messages in India?

A: Eagle
B: Peacock
C: Pigeon
D: Sparrow

If you would like to use your 50:50 please turn to page 205
If you would like to Ask The Audience please turn to page 217
Turn to the answer section on page 229 to find out if you've won ₹10,000

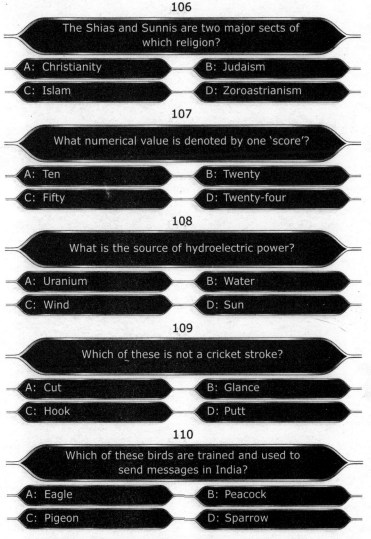

111

Which of these is not associated with the number twelve?

A: Decade

B: Dozen

C: Midnight

D: Noon

112

Which of these fruits is not divided into various segments inside?

A: Pomegranate

B: Orange

C: Mango

D: Sweet Lime

113

Which of these professionals is associated with the term 'bookkeeping'?

A: Scientists

B: Painters

C: Accountants

D: Librarians

114

In which sport do contestants wear a mouthpiece for protection?

A: Boxing

B: Cricket

C: Sumo

D: Fencing

115

Which of these natural fibres is derived from the seed-hair of a plant?

A: Silk

B: Jute

C: Wool

D: Cotton

If you would like to use your 50:50 please turn to page 205
If you would like to Ask The Audience please turn to page 217
Turn to the answer section on page 229 to find out if you've won ₹10,000

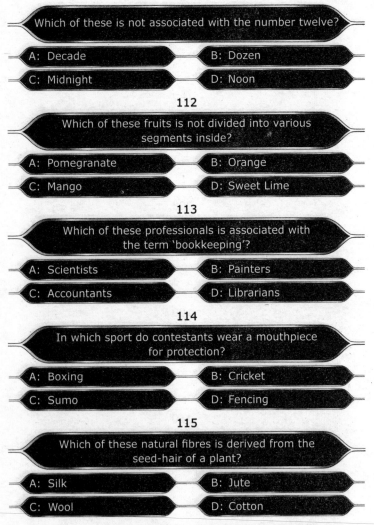

116

In cricket, which light does the third umpire switch on to indicate an 'out'?

A: Red
B: Green
C: Blue
D: Yellow

117

Which of these materials is not derived from animals or insects?

A: Leather
B: Silk
C: Wool
D: Cotton

118

To which specialist would you go for a root canal treatment?

A: Orthopaedist
B: Architect
C: Dentist
D: Opthalmologist

119

Which of these animals is also known as 'Jumbo'?

A: Lion
B: Tiger
C: Elephant
D: Rhinoceros

120

What is the sum total of all the angles of a right angled triangle?

A: 90 degrees
B: 180 degrees
C: 60 degrees
D: 45 degrees

If you would like to use your 50:50 please turn to page 206
If you would like to Ask The Audience please turn to page 218
Turn to the answer section on page 229 to find out if you've won ₹10,000

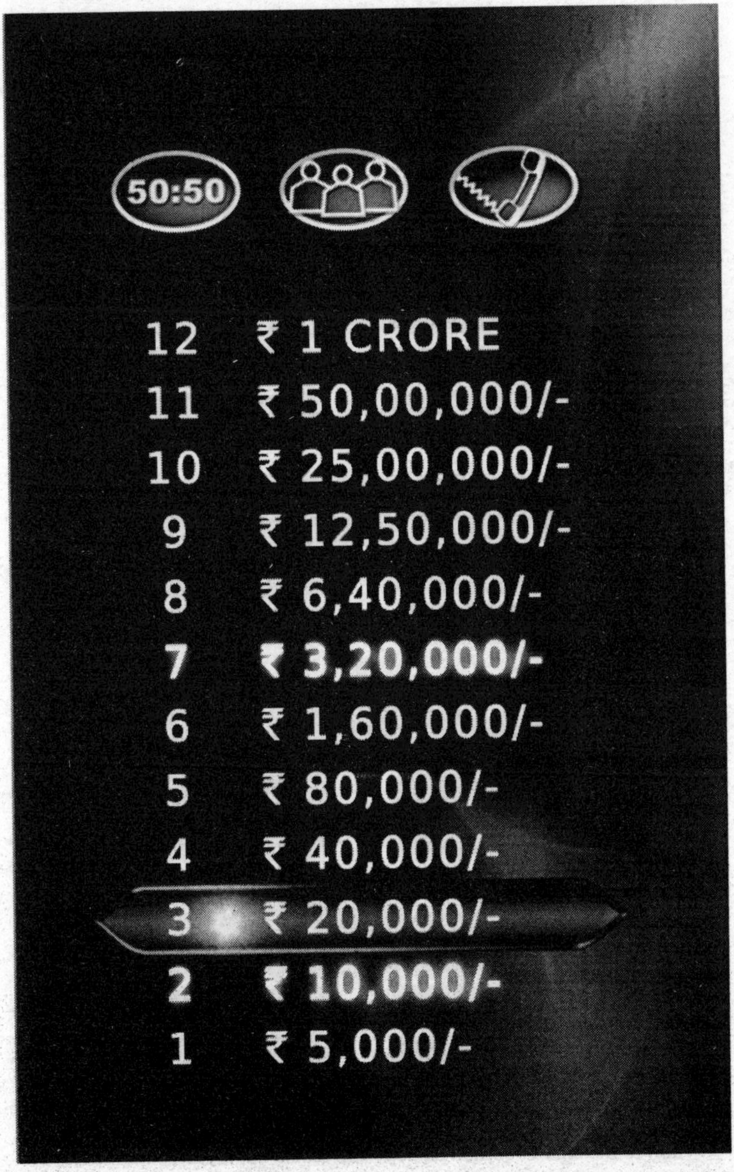
50:50
12 ₹ 1 CRORE
11 ₹ 50,00,000/-
10 ₹ 25,00,000/-
9 ₹ 12,50,000/-
8 ₹ 6,40,000/-
7 ₹ 3,20,000/-
6 ₹ 1,60,000/-
5 ₹ 80,000/-
4 ₹ 40,000/-
3 ₹ 20,000/-
2 ₹ 10,000/-
1 ₹ 5,000/-

3 ♦ ₹20,000

1

Which planned city is named after the fortress temple of Chandi?

A: Chandernagore

B: Chandigarh

C: Chandipur-on-Sea

D: Chandrapur

2

In tennis, what is the numeric value of the first point won by a player?

A: 25

B: 5

C: 10

D: 15

3

In which of the following films did Juhi Chawla not act?

A: Darr

B: Swades

C: Duplicate

D: Yes Boss

4

Which two numbers together form the 'binary language' used in computers?

A: 0 & 9

B: 1 & 3

C: 0 & 1

D: 1 & 2

5

Which community's New Year Day is called Navroz?

A: Sikhs

B: Parsis

C: Christians

D: Muslims

If you would like to use your 50:50 please turn to page 206
If you would like to Ask The Audience please turn to page 218
Turn to the answer section on page 229 to find out if you've won ₹20,000

6

Which is the highest mountain peak in the world?

A: K2
B: Nanga Parbat
C: Mt. Everest
D: Kanchenjunga

7

According to the zodiac, what is the birth sign of Jesus Christ?

A: Aquarius
B: Capricorn
C: Sagittarius
D: Scorpio

8

Who was Arjuna's charioteer during the battle of Kurukshetra?

A: Salya
B: Sanjay
C: Krishna
D: Uttara Kumar

9

Which of the following body parts does a snake have?

A: Eyelids
B: Legs
C: Tongue
D: Ears

10

In which of these services will you find a Wing Commander?

A: Army
B: Air Force
C: Police
D: Navy

If you would like to use your 50:50 please turn to page 206
If you would like to Ask The Audience please turn to page 218
Turn to the answer section on page 229 to find out if you've won ₹20,000

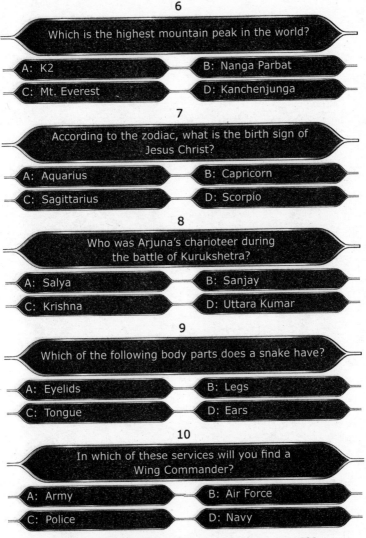

11

The diseases of which part of the body are treated by a dermatologist?

A: Eyes
B: Skin
C: Ears
D: Kidney

12

How many years make a millennium?

A: One Thousand
B: One Hundred
C: Ten Thousand
D: One Million

13

Who played the female lead actor in the 1995 film 'Rangeela'?

A: Shilpa Shetty
B: Namrata Shirodkar
C: Rambha
D: Urmila Matondkar

14

Through which of these parts do fish usually breathe?

A: Ears
B: Fins
C: Gills
D: Lungs

15

Who was the son of Dasharatha and Kaikeyi in the Ramayana?

A: Lakshmana
B: Bharata
C: Rama
D: Shatrughna

If you would like to use your 50:50 please turn to page 206
If you would like to Ask The Audience please turn to page 218
Turn to the answer section on page 229 to find out if you've won ₹20,000

16

Which of the following trees has aerial roots?

A: Neem
B: Banyan
C: Coconut
D: Peepal

17

Which of these monuments is in Kolkata?

A: India Gate
B: Gateway of India
C: Victoria Memorial
D: Vidhana Soudha

18

Which of these films is not directed by Ram Gopal Varma?

A: Bhoot
B: Sarkar
C: Company
D: Shool

19

Which of these is not one of the four Vedas?

A: Sama Veda
B: Rig Veda
C: Ayurveda
D: Atharva Veda

20

Normally, which of these sports is played on AstroTurf?

A: Hockey
B: Cricket
C: Polo
D: Table Tennis

If you would like to use your 50:50 please turn to page 206
If you would like to Ask The Audience please turn to page 218
Turn to the answer section on page 229 to find out if you've won ₹20,000

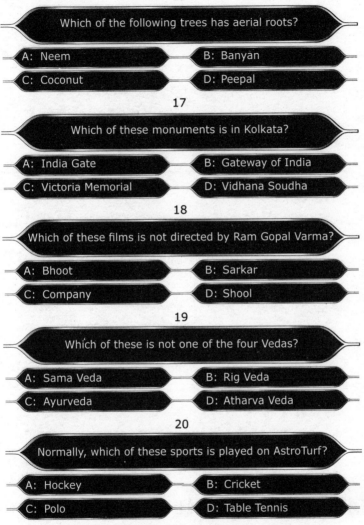

21

If an object reflects no light, what colour would it be?

A: White
B: Pink
C: Blue
D: Black

22

How many zeroes are there in one lakh?

A: Four
B: Five
C: Six
D: Seven

23

Which of these Indian states is landlocked?

A: Karnataka
B: Tamil Nadu
C: Bihar
D: Gujarat

24

In the Ramayana, who was the mother of Luv and Kush?

A: Urmila
B: Sita
C: Mandodari
D: Mandavi

25

Who is the youngest Indian to play Test cricket?

A: Sachin Tendulkar
B: Harbhajan Singh
C: Sourav Ganguly
D: Narendra Hirwani

If you would like to use your 50:50 please turn to page 206
If you would like to Ask The Audience please turn to page 218
Turn to the answer section on page 229 to find out if you've won ₹20,000

26

The Wagah checkpost lies on India's border with which country?

A: China
B: Myanmar
C: Nepal
D: Pakistan

27

Which of these sports items is normally made of plastic?

A: Discus
B: Javelin
C: Table Tennis Ball
D: Shot Put

28

Which of the following natural resources is inexhaustible?

A: Natural Gas
B: Iron Ore
C: Coal
D: Solar Energy

29

Eskimos are natives of which region?

A: Arctic
B: Australia
C: Antarctica
D: Estonia

30

Which instrument is used to measure temperature?

A: Barometer
B: Thermometer
C: Nanometer
D: Galvanometer

If you would like to use your 50:50 please turn to page 206
If you would like to Ask The Audience please turn to page 218
Turn to the answer section on page 229 to find out if you've won ₹20,000

31

Which of these birds is strictly the male of its species?

A: Sparrow
B: Woodpecker
C: Hen
D: Peacock

32

In Hindu mythology, whose wife is Lakshmi?

A: Brahma
B: Vishnu
C: Shiva
D: Ganesha

33

Which of these films stars Shah Rukh Khan and Juhi Chawla?

A: Nau Do Gyarah
B: Do aur Do Panch
C: Do Dooni Char
D: One 2 Ka 4

34

Which of the following is located south of the equator?

A: Taj Mahal
B: Statue of Liberty
C: Eiffel Tower
D: None of these

35

Which century would the year 1650 be in?

A: 15th
B: 16th
C: 17th
D: 14th

If you would like to use your 50:50 please turn to page 206
If you would like to Ask The Audience please turn to page 218
Turn to the answer section on page 229 to find out if you've won ₹20,000

36

What is the mathematical term that means 'without end' or 'limitless'?

A: Infinity
B: Zero
C: Decimal
D: Calculus

37

During which of these situations might a Caesarian operation be performed?

A: Heart Attack
B: Brain Tumour
C: Haemorrhage
D: Childbirth

38

At which of these places would you find a caddie?

A: Car Park
B: Zoo
C: Golf Course
D: Market

39

The Golden Temple Mail connects which city to Mumbai by rail?

A: Amritsar
B: Allahabad
C: Jalandhar
D: Chennai

40

Where would you find the Empire State Building?

A: Chicago
B: Paris
C: New York City
D: London

If you would like to use your 50:50 please turn to page 206
If you would like to Ask The Audience please turn to page 218
Turn to the answer section on page 229 to find out if you've won ₹20,000

41

Which symbol is used to indicate facilities for the physically challenged?

A: Walking Stick
B: Wheelchair
C: Crutch
D: Eye-patch

42

What substance is normally used to disinfect water in a swimming pool?

A: Chlorine
B: Ammonia
C: Argon
D: Neon

43

In the Mahabharata, what was Draupadi's name at birth?

A: Krishna
B: Mandvi
C: Savitri
D: Satyavati

44

What is the sum total of all the numbers from 1 to 10?

A: Forty-five
B: Fifty
C: Fifty-five
D: Sixty

45

Which one of these sports equipment is the lightest?

A: Shot
B: Discus
C: Hammer
D: Javelin

If you would like to use your 50:50 please turn to page 206
If you would like to Ask The Audience please turn to page 218
Turn to the answer section on page 229 to find out if you've won ₹20,000

46

Fiat cars were originally made in which country?

A: Italy
B: England
C: Russia
D: Germany

47

In which sea or ocean is the island nation of Maldives located?

A: Indian Ocean
B: Arabian Sea
C: Bay of Bengal
D: Pacific Ocean

48

In the fairy tale, how many dwarfs did Snow White meet in the forest?

A: Three
B: Six
C: Five
D: Seven

49

Which of these terms does not refer to a playing position in football?

A: Half-back
B: Full-back
C: Draw-back
D: Stopper

50

Which of the following is not one of the five 'K's of Sikhism?

A: Kesh
B: Kachcha
C: Kundal
D: Kirpan

If you would like to use your 50:50 please turn to page 206
If you would like to Ask The Audience please turn to page 218
Turn to the answer section on page 229 to find out if you've won ₹20,000

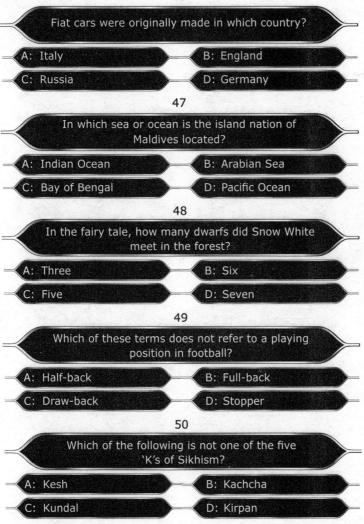

51

Where in the human body is the cornea?

A: Eyes
B: Nose
C: Brain
D: Ears

52

Which avatar of Vishnu is also known as Govinda?

A: Rama
B: Krishna
C: Parashurama
D: Kalki

53

What does the letter 'C' stand for in the insurance firm LIC ?

A: Commission
B: Corporation
C: Company
D: Cell

54

What is the minimum educational qualification required to become an MLA?

A: Matriculation
B: Graduation
C: Standard Five
D: None

55

In which of the following games is the term 'deuce' used?

A: Golf
B: Tennis
C: Chess
D: Billiards

If you would like to use your 50:50 please turn to page 206
If you would like to Ask The Audience please turn to page 218
Turn to the answer section on page 229 to find out if you've won ₹20,000

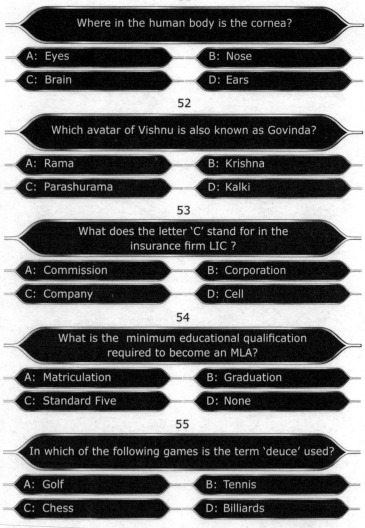

56

Which of these would not be used to put out a fire?

A: Water
B: Sand
C: Oxygen
D: Carbon Dioxide

57

Which is the largest animal in the world?

A: Elephant
B: Giraffe
C: Blue Whale
D: Orangutan

58

In which zone of the Ranji Trophy cricket tournament does Delhi take part?

A: North
B: South
C: West
D: Central

59

Which Hindu god's vahana is a 'mushak' or rat?

A: Vishnu
B: Ganesha
C: Shiva
D: Brahma

60

Who played Saira Banu's music teacher in the Hindi film 'Padosan'?

A: Jagdeep
B: Kishore Kumar
C: Keshto Mukherjee
D: Mehmood

If you would like to use your 50:50 please turn to page 206
If you would like to Ask The Audience please turn to page 218
Turn to the answer section on page 229 to find out if you've won ₹20,000

61

Which of these hill stations is also the capital of a state?

A: Mahabaleshwar
B: Mount Abu
C: Udhagamandalam
D: Shimla

62

With which Hindu deity is the ISKCON movement associated?

A: Ganesha
B: Shiva
C: Krishna
D: Brahma

63

What are backstroke, breaststroke and butterfly types of?

A: Tennis strokes
B: Massage strokes
C: Flying techniques
D: Swimming strokes

64

How many times does the digit '1' appear from 0 to 100?

A: Twenty-two
B: Eleven
C: Twenty-one
D: Eighteen

65

The Koala bear prefers to feed on the leaves of which tree?

A: Pine
B: Eucalyptus
C: Teak
D: Bamboo

If you would like to use your 50:50 please turn to page 206
If you would like to Ask The Audience please turn to page 218
Turn to the answer section on page 229 to find out if you've won ₹20,000

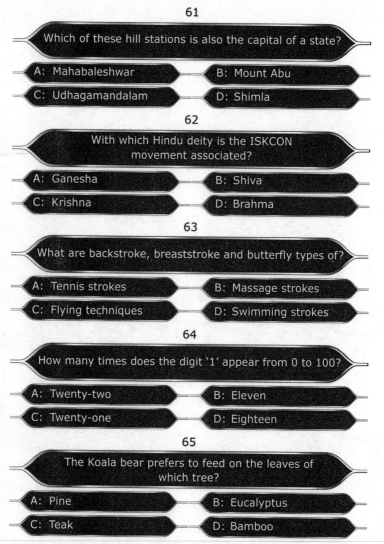

66

In the Ramayana, Jambavan leads a force comprising which animals?

A: Vultures
B: Bears
C: Eagles
D: Monkeys

67

Which two colours feature on the national flag of Bangladesh?

A: Green - Red
B: Green - White
C: Red - White
D: Red - Yellow

68

In which country is the Wimbledon tennis tournament held?

A: USA
B: Australia
C: France
D: England

69

In radio transmission, what does 'MW' stand for?

A: Mini Wavelength
B: Mostly Western
C: Medium Wave
D: Micro Wave

70

A ball of what colour is used in a day and night cricket match?

A: Red
B: White
C: Yellow
D: Black and White

If you would like to use your 50:50 please turn to page 206
If you would like to Ask The Audience please turn to page 218
Turn to the answer section on page 229 to find out if you've won ₹20,000

71

In Hindu tradition, who is also called Maheshwara?

A: Rama
B: Vishnu
C: Shiva
D: Yama

72

Which of these actors did not star in the Hindi film 'Mera Naam Joker'?

A: Manoj Kumar
B: Dharmendra
C: Raaj Kumar
D: Rajendra Kumar

73

Which of these islands is a part of India?

A: Mauritius
B: Minicoy
C: Madagascar
D: Malta

74

What does the letter 'W' on an electric bulb indicate?

A: Weight
B: Warning
C: Watt
D: Wainwright

75

What is 100 percent of 225?

A: 2250
B: 250
C: 225
D: 25

If you would like to use your 50:50 please turn to page 206
If you would like to Ask The Audience please turn to page 218
Turn to the answer section on page 229 to find out if you've won ₹20,000

76

Through which of these states does the River Ganga not flow?

A: Uttar Pradesh
B: Bihar
C: West Bengal
D: Chhattisgarh

77

Which of these would you use to increase the travelling speed of a car?

A: Brake
B: Accelerator
C: Clutch
D: Carburettor

78

What is a class of animals that can live both on land and in water called?

A: Reptiles
B: Amphibians
C: Mammals
D: Marsupials

79

What is the equivalent of 'chaar anna' in decimal currency?

A: 75 paise
B: 50 paise
C: 100 paise
D: 25 paise

80

In which of these films did Aamir Khan play the role of a taxi driver?

A: Ghulam
B: Raja Hindustani
C: Rangeela
D: Taare Zameen Par

If you would like to use your 50:50 please turn to page 207
If you would like to Ask The Audience please turn to page 219
Turn to the answer section on page 229 to find out if you've won ₹20,000

81

Which of these regions is in Rajasthan?

A: Kathiawar
B: Mewar
C: Saurashtra
D: Kutch

82

Traditionally, which animals pull Santa Claus' sleigh?

A: Dogs
B: Horses
C: Reindeer
D: Polar Bears

83

How many spokes appear in the chakra or wheel on the Indian national flag?

A: Twenty-four
B: Forty-eight
C: Sixteen
D: Thirty-two

84

Who played Anarkali in the film 'Mughal-e-Azam'?

A: Meena Kumari
B: Madhubala
C: Nutan
D: Nargis

85

In a Test match, who would normally wear a white coat on the field?

A: Wicket-keeper
B: Bowler
C: Batsman
D: Umpire

If you would like to use your 50:50 please turn to page 207
If you would like to Ask The Audience please turn to page 219
Turn to the answer section on page 229 to find out if you've won ₹20,000

86

What comes in sizes A3, A4 and A5?

A: Carpets
B: Guns
C: Paper
D: Televisions

87

Which of these is not a kind of dog?

A: German Shepherd
B: Bull Terrier
C: Chihuahua
D: Siamese

88

What is the term of office of the President of India?

A: Four years
B: Three years
C: Five years
D: Six years

89

Which of these is the principal export of Saudi Arabia?

A: Sand
B: Crude Oil
C: Cotton
D: Leather

90

With which sport would you associate a 'Golden Goal'?

A: Polo
B: Water Polo
C: Football
D: Hockey

If you would like to use your 50:50 please turn to page 207
If you would like to Ask The Audience please turn to page 219
Turn to the answer section on page 229 to find out if you've won ₹20,000

91

In the Ramayana, who was Ravana's chief queen?

A: Urmila
B: Sulochana
C: Mandodari
D: Menaka

92

Which of these is not a mountain range?

A: Aravalli
B: Satpura
C: Vindhya
D: Tunghabhadra

93

From which animal is musk or 'kasturi' extracted?

A: Lion
B: Deer
C: Camel
D: Goat

94

In terms of area, which is the largest country in the world?

A: Russia
B: China
C: USA
D: Canada

95

On a standard playing dice what number is directly opposite to one?

A: Four
B: Two
C: Six
D: Five

If you would like to use your 50:50 please turn to page 207
If you would like to Ask The Audience please turn to page 219
Turn to the answer section on page 229 to find out if you've won ₹20,000

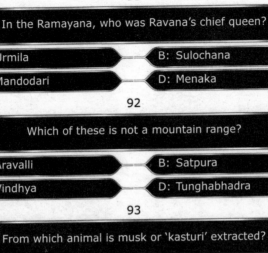

96

In which of these sports might a player commit a double fault?

A: Cricket
B: Polo
C: Golf
D: Tennis

97

In the Chinese practice of acupuncture, what is used to relieve pain?

A: Chopsticks
B: Needles
C: Kung-Fu
D: Ajinomoto

98

How many times does the phrase 'Jaya He' appear in our national anthem?

A: Six
B: Nine
C: Five
D: Eight

99

On which part of the human body is the ECG test performed?

A: Liver
B: Stomach
C: Brain
D: Heart

100

Which of the Pandavas did Draupadi garland at her swayamvara?

A: Arjuna
B: Bhima
C: Yudhishthira
D: Nakul

If you would like to use your 50:50 please turn to page 207
If you would like to Ask The Audience please turn to page 219
Turn to the answer section on page 229 to find out if you've won ₹20,000

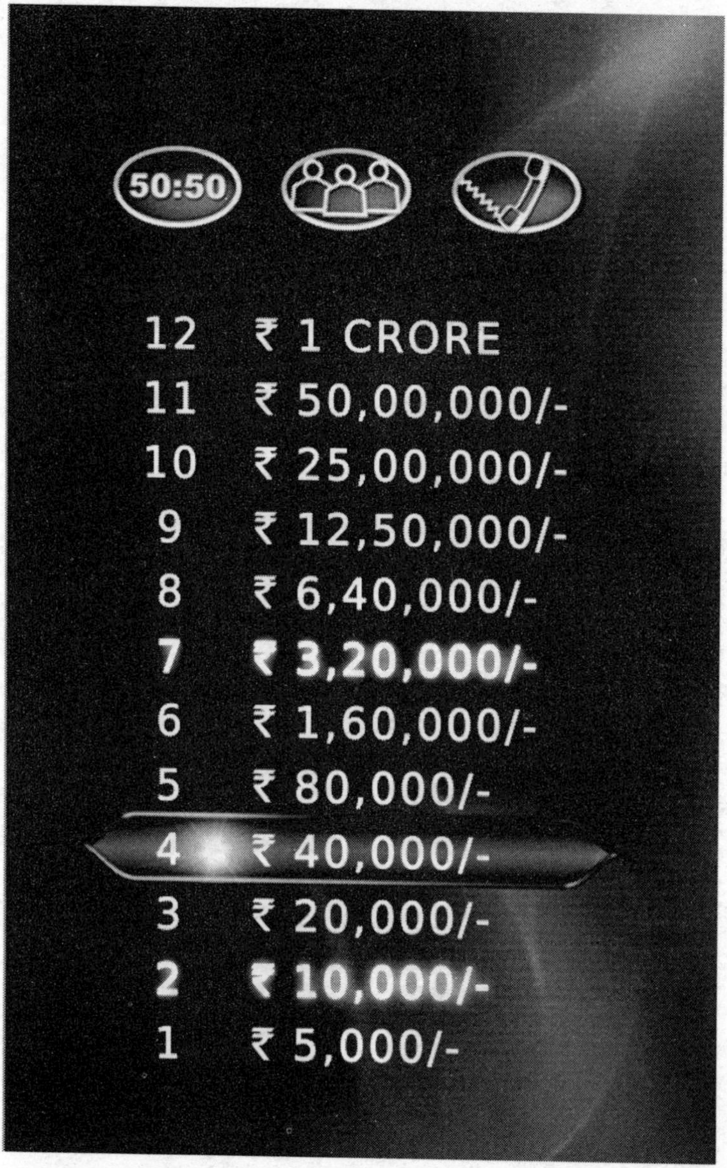
50:50
12 ₹ 1 CRORE
11 ₹ 50,00,000/-
10 ₹ 25,00,000/-
9 ₹ 12,50,000/-
8 ₹ 6,40,000/-
7 ₹ 3,20,000/-
6 ₹ 1,60,000/-
5 ₹ 80,000/-
4 ₹ 40,000/-
3 ₹ 20,000/-
2 ₹ 10,000/-
1 ₹ 5,000/-

4 ♦ ₹40,000

1

Which gods are jointly worshipped under the title 'Hari-Hara'?

A: Shiva & Brahma
B: Brahma & Vishnu
C: Vishnu & Shiva
D: Ganesh & Indra

2

Which of the following paths does light take to travel?

A: Straight Line
B: Curved Line
C: Circular Line
D: Randomly

3

Which boxer's real name is Cassius Clay?

A: Mike Tyson
B: Muhammad Ali
C: Sonny Liston
D: Roberto Duran

4

Which of these rulers did not belong to the Mughal dynasty?

A: Akbar
B: Jahangir
C: Sher Shah Suri
D: Shah Jahan

5

Which is the hardest substance in the human body?

A: Skull Bones
B: Tooth Enamel
C: Kneecap
D: Finger Nail

If you would like to use your 50:50 please turn to page 207
If you would like to Ask The Audience please turn to page 219
Turn to the answer section on page 230 to find out if you've won ₹40,000

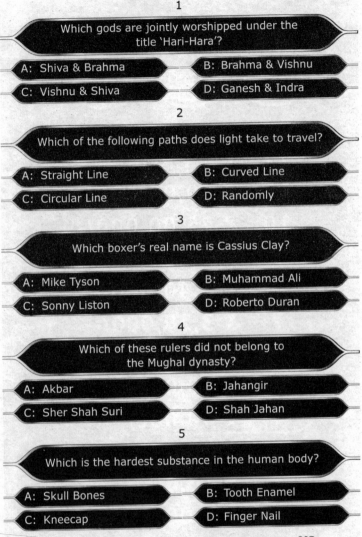

6

Which of these actresses has never been married to a sports person?

A: Sharmila Tagore
B: Sangeeta Bijlani
C: Reena Roy
D: Mumtaz

7

What is the Japanese art of folding paper into decorative objects called?

A: Kamikaze
B: Bonsai
C: Origami
D: Sushi

8

Gidda is a traditional folk dance form of which Indian state?

A: Gujarat
B: Punjab
C: Orissa
D: Kerala

9

In Islam, what is Prophet Muhammad's flight from Mecca to Medina known as?

A: Hejira
B: Fiqh
C: Haj
D: Safar

10

Which layer of gas surrounds the Earth 30 kms above its surface?

A: Ozone
B: Nitrogen
C: Carbon Dioxide
D: Oxygen

If you would like to use your 50:50 please turn to page 207
If you would like to Ask The Audience please turn to page 219
Turn to the answer section on page 230 to find out if you've won ₹40,000

11

On which city was the first atom bomb dropped?

A: Hiroshima
B: Tokyo
C: Okinawa
D: Nagasaki

12

What is the place of worship of the Jews called?

A: Chateau
B: Church
C: Synagogue
D: Fire Temple

13

What does an eyepower of 6/6 indicate?

A: Total Blindness
B: Partial Blindness
C: Normal Eyesight
D: Myopia

14

What are 747s, DC-8s and Do-228s?

A: Jeeps
B: Missiles
C: Trucks
D: Aeroplanes

15

Which of these is not found in India in the wild?

A: Leopard
B: Tiger
C: Lion
D: Puma

If you would like to use your 50:50 please turn to page 207
If you would like to Ask The Audience please turn to page 219
Turn to the answer section on page 230 to find out if you've won ₹40,000

16

In the Mahabharata, who demanded Eklavya's thumb as 'guru dakshina'?

A: Kripacharya
B: Parashurama
C: Dronacharya
D: Kirtivarma

17

Which planet is known as the 'Morning Star' as well as the 'Evening Star'?

A: Mars
B: Saturn
C: Venus
D: Jupiter

18

Who was the first Muslim president of India?

A: Maulana Azad
B: Zakir Hussain
C: Abul Kalam Azad
D: Fakhruddin Ali Ahmed

19

What is the equivalent of '0' degree Centigrade on the Fahrenheit scale?

A: 32 degrees
B: 132 degrees
C: 0 degrees
D: 100 degrees

20

In which country is Ghazni located?

A: Mongolia
B: Afghanistan
C: Iran
D: Iraq

If you would like to use your 50:50 please turn to page 207
If you would like to Ask The Audience please turn to page 219
Turn to the answer section on page 230 to find out if you've won ₹40,000

21

Who has written the bhajan 'Mere to Giridhar Gopal, Doosro Na Koi'?

A: Surdas
B: Narsinh Mehta
C: Mirabai
D: Chaitanya

22

Which of these diseases is caused by a vitamin deficiency?

A: Cholera
B: Plague
C: Rickets
D: Typhoid

23

In Indian taxation terminology, what does the 'P' in PAN stand for?

A: Permanent
B: Private
C: Personal
D: Public

24

On the banks of which river is Ayodhya situated?

A: Tapti
B: Sarayu
C: Yamuna
D: Ganga

25

Which part of a camera opens to admit light when you take a photo?

A: Flash
B: Lens
C: Shutter
D: Film

If you would like to use your 50:50 please turn to page 207
If you would like to Ask The Audience please turn to page 219
Turn to the answer section on page 230 to find out if you've won ₹40,000

26

Which comic character is known as 'The Ghost Who Walks'?

A: Mandrake
B: Flash Gordon
C: Phantom
D: Spiderman

27

In which language were the sacred scriptures of Islam, the Koran, written?

A: Persian
B: Arabic
C: Hebrew
D: Urdu

28

What was the nationality of the first human being to step on the Moon?

A: Russian
B: French
C: American
D: Chinese

29

What is the hardest known substance?

A: Granite
B: Diamond
C: Graphite
D: Talc

30

Which part of a person's eye determines its colour?

A: Pupil
B: Cornea
C: Retina
D: Iris

If you would like to use your 50:50 please turn to page 207
If you would like to Ask The Audience please turn to page 219
Turn to the answer section on page 230 to find out if you've won ₹40,000

31

In which continent is 90% of the world's rice grown?

A: South America
B: Europe
C: Africa
D: Asia

32

Which artist and inventor painted the world-famous 'Mona Lisa'?

A: Michelangelo
B: Leonardo da Vinci
C: Raphael
D: Bellini

33

The name of which state literally means 'The Land of Gems'?

A: Nagaland
B: Manipur
C: Mizoram
D: Meghalaya

34

In the Mahabharata, what was the capital of the Kauravas?

A: Hastinapur
B: Mathura
C: Indraprastha
D: Kaushambhi

35

The flag of which neighbouring country of India bears five stars?

A: Pakistan
B: Bhutan
C: China
D: Bangladesh

If you would like to use your 50:50 please turn to page 207
If you would like to Ask The Audience please turn to page 219
Turn to the answer section on page 230 to find out if you've won ₹40,000

36

In Congress (I), what does 'I' stand for?

A: International
B: Indira
C: Indian
D: Independent

37

Which of these Sufi saints was Amir Khusro a disciple of?

A: Bulle Shah
B: Baba Farid
C: Nizamuddin Auliya
D: Sarmad

38

According to Hindu legend, which stone transforms iron into gold?

A: Paras
B: Panna
C: Firoza
D: Neelam

39

Who played the title role of the cook in the film 'Bawarchi'?

A: Rajesh Khanna
B: Sanjeev Kumar
C: Vinod Mehra
D: Dharmendra

40

After which war did King Ashoka renounce war?

A: Magadha
B: Kalinga
C: Avanti
D: Koshala

If you would like to use your 50:50 please turn to page 207
If you would like to Ask The Audience please turn to page 219
Turn to the answer section on page 230 to find out if you've won ₹40,000

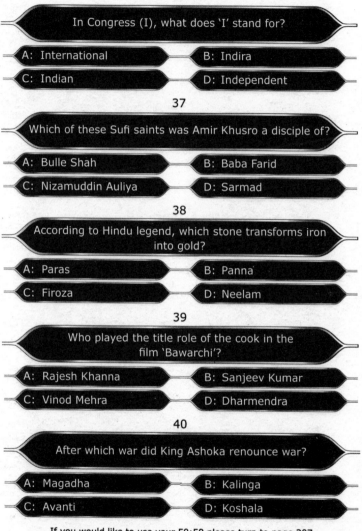

41

What substance gives human blood its distinctive red colour?

A: Insulin
B: Haemoglobin
C: Oxygen
D: Albumin

42

The spiritual leaders of which religion were known as 'Tirthankaras'?

A: Sikhism
B: Buddhism
C: Hinduism
D: Jainism

43

In 1948, who founded the RK Studios?

A: Prithviraj Kapoor
B: Shammi Kapoor
C: Raj Kapoor
D: Shashi Kapoor

44

In which Asian country are the islands of Sumatra, Java and Bali?

A: Sri Lanka
B: Indonesia
C: Malaysia
D: Philippines

45

Which of these is commonly used as a bleaching agent?

A: Hydrogen Peroxide
B: Sodium Chloride
C: Hydrogen Chloride
D: Copper Sulphate

If you would like to use your 50:50 please turn to page 207
If you would like to Ask The Audience please turn to page 219
Turn to the answer section on page 230 to find out if you've won ₹40,000

46

What is the background colour of the Olympic flag?

A: Blue
B: Red
C: Black
D: White

47

Which of these languages is not written in Devanagari script?

A: Sanskrit
B: Hindi
C: Marathi
D: Urdu

48

What is the title of the head of the Roman Catholic church?

A: Pope
B: Grand Master
C: Cardinal
D: Caesar

49

Ozone is an allotrope of which element?

A: Carbon
B: Hydrogen
C: Sulphur
D: Oxygen

50

In Hindu mythology, which of these queens married through a swayamwara?

A: Subhadra
B: Gandhari
C: Urvashi
D: Sita

If you would like to use your 50:50 please turn to page 207
If you would like to Ask The Audience please turn to page 219
Turn to the answer section on page 230 to find out if you've won ₹40,000

51

Which of these drinks is of Russian origin?

A: Sherry
B: Vodka
C: Brandy
D: Champagne

52

Which of these organs of the human body is found in a pair?

A: Gall Bladder
B: Stomach
C: Kidney
D: Liver

53

In the Ramayana, who among these was not a daughter-in-law of Dasharatha?

A: Urmila
B: Sumitra
C: Shrutakirti
D: Mandavi

54

Which of these is a helicopter used by the Indian Air Force?

A: Chakra
B: Cheetah
C: Chandra
D: Chakravyuha

55

Which of these rivers is a tributary of the Ganga?

A: Beas
B: Godavari
C: Gomti
D: Mahanadi

If you would like to use your 50:50 please turn to page 207
If you would like to Ask The Audience please turn to page 219
Turn to the answer section on page 230 to find out if you've won ₹40,000

56

Who among these has served as the Chief Election Commissioner of India?

A: P N Haksar
B: Manmohan Singh
C: T N Seshan
D: R K Dhawan

57

To obtain what did the Asuras and Devas churn the ocean?

A: Vajra
B: Amrit
C: Brahmastra
D: Divyadrishti

58

In tennis, which term is used to denote the score of forty all?

A: Love
B: Deuce
C: Ace
D: Break Point

59

A compound of which of these metals is used in photography?

A: Iron
B: Calcium
C: Silver
D: Gold

60

What does the 'C' in CAT Scan stand for?

A: Cranial
B: Computerised
C: Coronary
D: Carotid

If you would like to use your 50:50 please turn to page 208
If you would like to Ask The Audience please turn to page 220
Turn to the answer section on page 230 to find out if you've won ₹40,000

61

Which princely state's rulers bore the title of 'Nizam'?

A: Mysore
B: Hyderabad
C: Arcot
D: Gwalior

62

Who among these is not a chess player?

A: Judith Polgar
B: Koneru Humpy
C: Veselin Topalov
D: Lance Armstrong

63

Which of these is a rank in the Indian Police Service?

A: General
B: Major General
C: Inspector General
D: Brigadier General

64

Who preached the doctrine of 'Ashtangika Marga' or the Eightfold Path?

A: Guru Nanak
B: Mahavira
C: Gautam Buddha
D: Swami Vivekananda

65

Which of these queens died of battle wounds?

A: Rani of Jhansi
B: Mumtaz Mahal
C: Jodha Bai
D: Ahilyabai Holkar

If you would like to use your 50:50 please turn to page 208
If you would like to Ask The Audience please turn to page 220
Turn to the answer section on page 230 to find out if you've won ₹40,000

66

In which country did Mahatma Gandhi study law?

A: Russia
B: South Africa
C: England
D: France

67

In the Mahabharata, who was born with 'kawach' and 'kundala'?

A: Arjuna
B: Yudhishthira
C: Karna
D: Bheeshma

68

Which of these countries is made up entirely of islands?

A: Japan
B: Malaysia
C: Mozambique
D: Greece

69

Which South African cricketer is nicknamed 'Zulu'?

A: Shaun Pollock
B: Lance Klusener
C: Jonty Rhodes
D: Gary Kirsten

70

Which is the largest gland in the human body?

A: Thyroid
B: Liver
C: Pancreas
D: Parotid

If you would like to use your 50:50 please turn to page 208
If you would like to Ask The Audience please turn to page 220
Turn to the answer section on page 230 to find out if you've won ₹40,000

71

According to Hindu mythology, who created the world?

A: Brahma
B: Vishnu
C: Shiva
D: Vishwakarma

72

Which is the only Asian member of the G-8 group?

A: Japan
B: China
C: India
D: Kuwait

73

How many women have been the President of the USA?

A: One
B: None
C: Four
D: Two

74

In the film 'Wanted', what was Salman Khan's actual profession?

A: Doctor
B: Police Officer
C: Lawyer
D: Underworld Don

75

Which of these countries is cricketer Geoffrey Boycott's native country?

A: Australia
B: Zimbabwe
C: South Africa
D: United Kingdom

If you would like to use your 50:50 please turn to page 208
If you would like to Ask The Audience please turn to page 220
Turn to the answer section on page 230 to find out if you've won ₹40,000

76

What is known as the 'Fourth Estate'?

A: Defence | B: Judiciary

C: Public | D: Press

77

Which Hindi film features the patriotic song 'Mere Desh Ki Dharti'?

A: Upkar | B: Kranti

C: Poorab aur Paschim | D: Shaheed

78

Which of these viruses causes AIDS?

A: Lactobacillus | B: HIV

C: Penicillium | D: Salmonella

79

In which of the following countries does one drive on the right side of the road?

A: India | B: Thailand

C: UK | D: USA

80

Which freedom fighter was also known as the 'Nightingale of India'?

A: Vijayalakshmi Pandit | B: Lata Mangeshkar

C: Rajkumari Amrit Kaur | D: Sarojini Naidu

If you would like to use your 50:50 please turn to page 208
If you would like to Ask The Audience please turn to page 220
Turn to the answer section on page 230 to find out if you've won ₹40,000

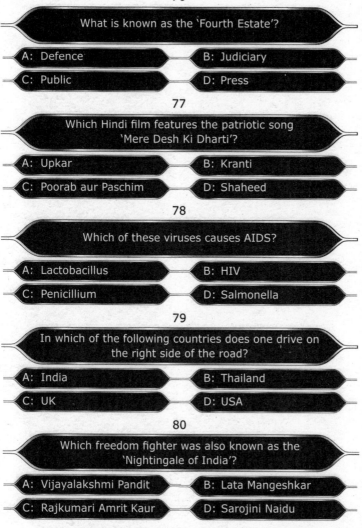

81

With which of these would you associate a 'black hole'?

A: Outer Space
B: Oceans
C: Earth's Centre
D: Blacksmith's Shop

82

Which of these persons played Test cricket for India?

A: Vijay Mallya
B: Vijay Tendulkar
C: Vijay Amritraj
D: Vijay Merchant

83

Which of these ages immediately preceded the Iron Age?

A: Ice
B: Bronze
C: Stone
D: Silver

84

A person of which of these blood groups is called a universal donor?

A: O
B: AB
C: B+
D: A+

85

Who was India's first woman Indian Police Service officer?

A: Santosh Yadav
B: Kalpana Chawla
C: Kiran Bedi
D: Bachendri Pal

If you would like to use your 50:50 please turn to page 208
If you would like to Ask The Audience please turn to page 220
Turn to the answer section on page 230 to find out if you've won ₹40,000

86

Who played Nargis' husband in the film 'Mother India'?

A: Sunil Dutt
B: Raaj Kumar
C: Rajendra Kumar
D: Kanhaiyalal

87

Baghdad is the capital of which country?

A: Afghanistan
B: Kuwait
C: Iraq
D: Saudi Arabia

88

Whose autobiography is titled 'Mein Kampf'?

A: Adolf Hitler
B: Otto Von Bismarck
C: Goethe
D: Friedrich Max Mueller

89

Sumo is a traditional form of wrestling of which country?

A: North Korea
B: Japan
C: South Korea
D: China

90

In the Ramayana, who was Sugreeva's elder brother?

A: Hanuman
B: Angad
C: Jambavan
D: Bali

If you would like to use your 50:50 please turn to page 208
If you would like to Ask The Audience please turn to page 220
Turn to the answer section on page 230 to find out if you've won ₹40,000

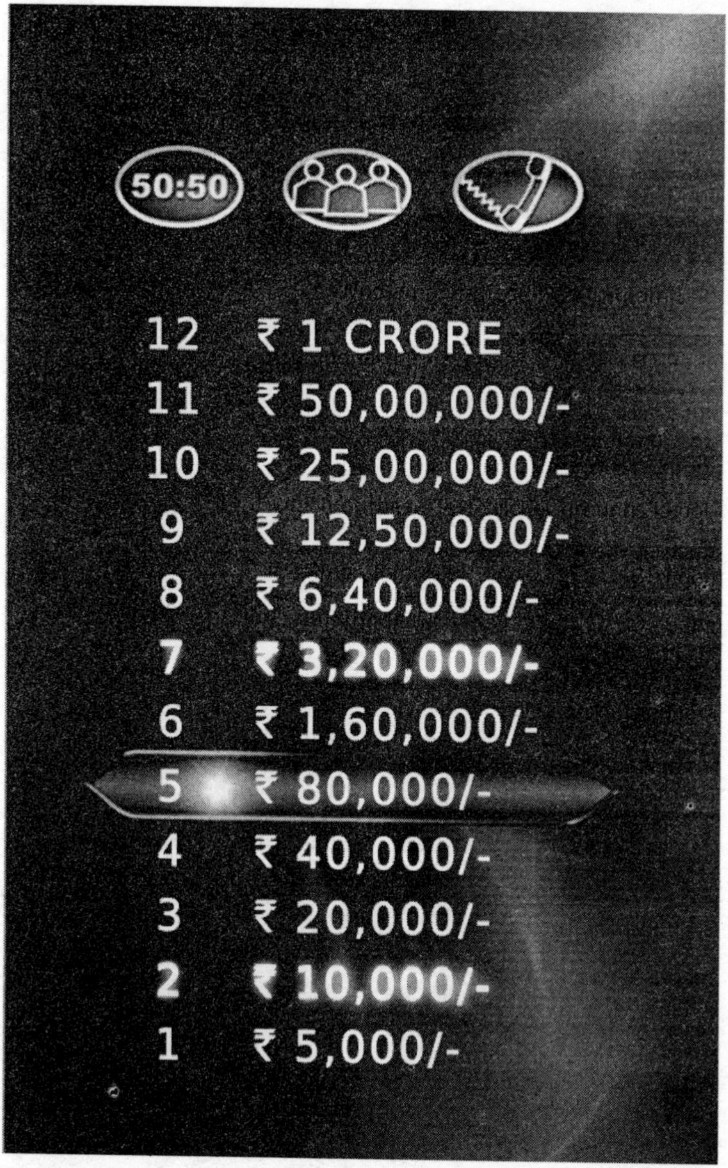
50:50
12 ₹ 1 CRORE
11 ₹ 50,00,000/-
10 ₹ 25,00,000/-
9 ₹ 12,50,000/-
8 ₹ 6,40,000/-
7 ₹ 3,20,000/-
6 ₹ 1,60,000/-
5 ₹ 80,000/-
4 ₹ 40,000/-
3 ₹ 20,000/-
2 ₹ 10,000/-
1 ₹ 5,000/-

5 ♦ ₹80,000

1

Which of these Hindi films did not star a former Miss India?

A: Partner

B: Vaastav

C: Dastak

D: Sarkar

2

In which sport is the Rovers Cup awarded?

A: Tennis

B: Football

C: Golf

D: Hockey

3

Who among these is a spiritual and religious leader of the Jews?

A: Padre

B: Maulvi

C: Rabbi

D: Sensei

4

Which galaxy is our Solar System a part of?

A: Milky Way

B: Alpha Centauri

C: Orion

D: Scorpion

5

Which leader was also called the 'Fuehrer'?

A: Stalin

B: Hitler

C: Idi Amin

D: Mussolini

If you would like to use your 50:50 please turn to page 208
If you would like to Ask The Audience please turn to page 220
Turn to the answer section on page 230 to find out if you've won ₹80,000

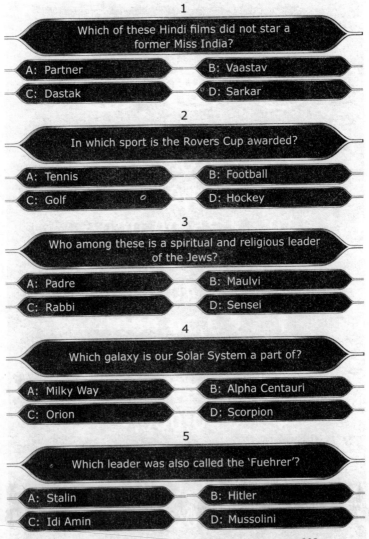

6

In Chacha Chaudhary comics, what is the name of Chacha Chaudhary's brother?

A: Chhajju Chowdhary
B: Chandu Chowdhary
C: Chamchu Chowdhary
D: Chinku Chowdhary

7

On malfunctioning of which of these organs is a person kept on dialysis?

A: Kidney
B: Heart
C: Liver
D: Lungs

8

Which of these countries has not won the Football World Cup for men?

A: Argentina
B: England
C: France
D: Russia

9

What are Shadaj, Madhyam, Pancham and Nishad names of?

A: Yogasanas
B: Musical Swaras
C: Dance Mudras
D: Mangoes

10

On what date is International Labour Day observed?

A: 2nd October
B: 1st May
C: 1st November
D: 1st March

If you would like to use your 50:50 please turn to page 208
If you would like to Ask The Audience please turn to page 220
Turn to the answer section on page 230 to find out if you've won ₹80,000

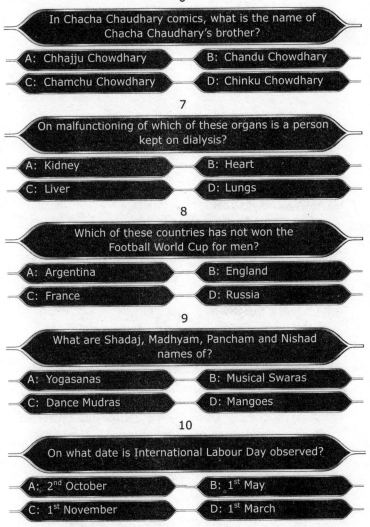

11

What is the nationality of the ancient philosopher Confucius?

A: Chinese
B: Italian
C: Portuguese
D: Japanese

12

Who became the first Indian to swim across the English Channel?

A: Mihir Sen
B: Taranath Shenoy
C: Anita Sood
D: Khazan Singh

13

Which of these Lok Sabha constituencies is not in Orissa?

A: Bhubaneswar
B: Koraput
C: Sambalpur
D: Hooghly

14

Who played the title role in the film 'Fiza'?

A: Rani Mukherjee
B: Karisma Kapoor
C: Kareena Kapoor
D: Preity Zinta

15

In an 'ektara', what is the resonator usually made of?

A: Pumpkin
B: Clay
C: Plywood
D: Coconut

If you would like to use your 50:50 please turn to page 208
If you would like to Ask The Audience please turn to page 220
Turn to the answer section on page 230 to find out if you've won ₹80,000

16

From which language have the words almirah and peon entered Indian usage?

A: Persian
B: Arabic
C: French
D: Portuguese

17

In which city located on the banks of River Shipra is the Kumbh Mela held?

A: Ujjain
B: Haridwar
C: Nasik
D: Prayag

18

Which is the world's heaviest land animal?

A: Hippopotamus
B: African Elephant
C: Polar Bear
D: Gorilla

19

How many historic battles were fought at Panipat between 1526 and 1761?

A: One
B: Four
C: Three
D: Two

20

Which of these is the lightest chemical element?

A: Helium
B: Oxygen
C: Hydrogen
D: Nitrogen

If you would like to use your 50:50 please turn to page 208
If you would like to Ask The Audience please turn to page 220
Turn to the answer section on page 230 to find out if you've won ₹80,000

21

In the Mahabharata, who was also known as 'Sutaputra'?

A: Arjuna
B: Ashwatthama
C: Shishupala
D: Karna

22

What is the atmospheric pressure in the hills in comparison to sea level?

A: Higher
B: Lower
C: Identical
D: Absent

23

Which famous singer played the title role in the 1935 film 'Devdas'?

A: Manna Dey
B: K L Saigal
C: Mukesh
D: C Ramachandran

24

A deficiency of which of the following vitamins causes night blindness?

A: Vitamin A
B: Vitamin B
C: Vitamin D
D: Vitamin C

25

Which bat and ball game is played by two teams with nine players each?

A: Cricket
B: Golf
C: Baseball
D: Netball

If you would like to use your 50:50 please turn to page 208
If you would like to Ask The Audience please turn to page 220
Turn to the answer section on page 230 to find out if you've won ₹80,000

26

Which of these ports is located on the east coast of India?

A: Kandla
B: Mumbai
C: Kochi
D: Machilipatnam

27

What was the name given to the first cloned sheep?

A: Sally
B: Polly
C: Dolly
D: Molly

28

Which one of these is the oldest of the four Vedas?

A: Rig Veda
B: Atharva Veda
C: Sama Veda
D: Yajur Veda

29

Who played the male lead in Bimal Roy's Hindi film 'Do Bigha Zamin'?

A: Dilip Kumar
B: Sunil Dutt
C: Raaj Kumar
D: Balraj Sahni

30

Which of these places in India is an island?

A: Karaikal
B: Diu
C: Dadra
D: Nagar Haveli

If you would like to use your 50:50 please turn to page 208
If you would like to Ask The Audience please turn to page 220
Turn to the answer section on page 230 to find out if you've won ₹80,000

31

Who built the forerunner of the Grand Trunk Road in the 16th century?

A: Ibrahim Lodi
B: Sher Shah Suri
C: Akbar
D: Rana Sanga

32

Which Pandava played the game of dice with Shakuni?

A: Arjuna
B: Yudhishthira
C: Bheema
D: Sahadeva

33

Which of these cities is not situated on the banks of the Ganga?

A: Haridwar
B: Bijnor
C: Mirzapur
D: Lucknow

34

What are lignite, anthracite and bituminous types of?

A: Petrol
B: Aluminium
C: Coal
D: Iron

35

Which of the following is a herbivorous animal?

A: Wolf
B: Fox
C: Rhinoceros
D: Mongoose

If you would like to use your 50:50 please turn to page 208
If you would like to Ask The Audience please turn to page 220
Turn to the answer section on page 230 to find out if you've won ₹80,000

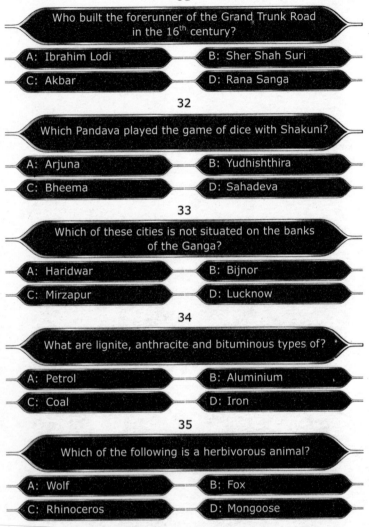

36

In which state are the hill stations of Dalhousie and Dharamsala located?

A: Sikkim
B: Himachal Pradesh
C: Uttarakhand
D: Jammu & Kashmir

37

Which Rajput hero became the king of Mewar in 1572?

A: Rana Sanga
B: Maharana Pratap
C: Bappa Rawal
D: Veer Hamir

38

Which of the following is not a month of the Saka calendar?

A: Shravana
B: Pausa
C: Bhadra
D: Sartha

39

Which of these winter sports activities is not performed in a rink?

A: Figure Skating
B: Ice Dancing
C: Ice Hockey
D: Skiing

40

In which direction does the earth rotate on its axis?

A: West to East
B: East to West
C: North to South
D: South to North

If you would like to use your 50:50 please turn to page 208
If you would like to Ask The Audience please turn to page 220
Turn to the answer section on page 230 to find out if you've won ₹80,000

41

According to the Ramayana, which of these was the mother of twin sons?

A: Kaikeyi
B: Sumitra
C: Kausalya
D: Tara

42

A lactometer is usually used to measure the density of which of these?

A: Water
B: Oil
C: Milk
D: Alcohol

43

Which of these is not a species of tiger?

A: Sumatran
B: Persian
C: Siberian
D: Bengal

44

Which of these rivers does not flow into the Bay of Bengal?

A: Tungabhadra
B: Mahanadi
C: Godavari
D: Narmada

45

On 21st December, the sun is directly over which of these imaginary lines?

A: Arctic Circle
B: Equator
C: Tropic of Cancer
D: Tropic of Capricorn

If you would like to use your 50:50 please turn to page 208
If you would like to Ask The Audience please turn to page 220
Turn to the answer section on page 230 to find out if you've won ₹80,000

46

Which Mughal Emperor built the Buland Darwaza at Fatehpur Sikri?

A: Humayun
B: Akbar
C: Babur
D: Shah Jahan

47

By what common name are Muslim migrants from India referred to in Pakistan?

A: Moplahs
B: Khidmatgars
C: Mohajirs
D: Razakars

48

Which land mammal has the longest gestation period?

A: Elephant
B: Man
C: Pig
D: Horse

49

Who is believed to have betrayed Jesus Christ after the Last Supper?

A: Jacob
B: Judas
C: John
D: Joshua

50

From which wood are cricket bats traditionally made?

A: Teak
B: Ebony
C: Willow
D: Balsa

If you would like to use your 50:50 please turn to page 209
If you would like to Ask The Audience please turn to page 221
Turn to the answer section on page 230 to find out if you've won ₹80,000

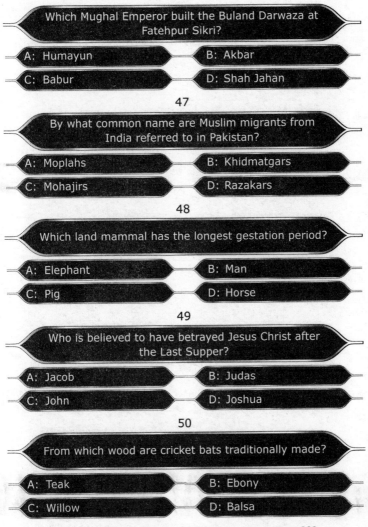

51

In which state are the towns of Margao and Vasco-da-Gama located?

A: Kerala
B: Maharashtra
C: Karnataka
D: Goa

52

Which part of an egg provides nourishment to the new life growing within?

A: Yolk
B: Albumen
C: Shell
D: Chalazae

53

Which character did Prithviraj Kapoor play in the film 'Mughal-e-Azam'?

A: Shah Jahan
B: Akbar
C: Tansen
D: Jahangir

54

In which European city would you find the Hyde Park?

A: London
B: Berlin
C: Paris
D: Amsterdam

55

Which Persian invader carried away the Peacock Throne from Delhi in 1739?

A: Ahmad Shah Abdali
B: Nadir Shah
C: Chenghiz Khan
D: Timur

If you would like to use your 50:50 please turn to page 209
If you would like to Ask The Audience please turn to page 221
Turn to the answer section on page 230 to find out if you've won ₹80,000

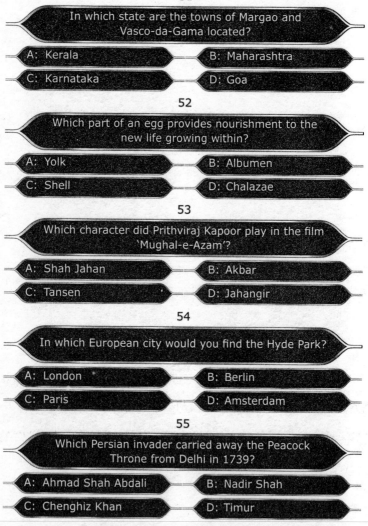

56

The flag of which of the following nations bears the 'Star of David'?

A: Pakistan
B: Israel
C: Vietnam
D: Cuba

57

Who among these was Gautam Buddha's son?

A: Siddhartha
B: Rahula
C: Ashoka
D: Kanthaka

58

Which of these Test cricket grounds is not located in India?

A: Green Park
B: Eden Gardens
C: Burlton Park
D: Sabina Park

59

Who crowned himself king of the Maratha kingdom in 1674?

A: Sambhaji
B: Balaji Vishwanath
C: Shivaji
D: Nana Saheb

60

In stereo equipment, what does the abbreviation 'Hi-Fi' mean?

A: High Frequency
B: High Fidelity
C: High Five
D: High Friction

If you would like to use your 50:50 please turn to page 209
If you would like to Ask The Audience please turn to page 221
Turn to the answer section on page 230 to find out if you've won ₹80,000

61

Which of the following is not an insect-borne disease?

A: Beriberi
B: Plague
C: Kala-azar
D: Malaria

62

How do we better know the actor Mohammed Kutty?

A: Mammootty
B: Thilakan
C: Baby Anthony
D: Mohanlal

63

On which river is the Bhakra dam situated?

A: Ravi
B: Beas
C: Sutlej
D: Jhelum

64

On which festive day did the Jallianwala Bagh massacre take place?

A: Basant Panchami
B: Baisakhi
C: Holi
D: Bhai Dooj

65

Who appoints the Governors of the states in India?

A: Prime Minister
B: Chief Minister
C: President
D: Chief Justice

If you would like to use your 50:50 please turn to page 209
If you would like to Ask The Audience please turn to page 221
Turn to the answer section on page 230 to find out if you've won ₹80,000

66

In 1953, along with Edmund Hillary, who reached the summit of Mt. Everest?

A: Ang Kami
B: Phu Dorjee
C: Tenzing Norgay
D: Sonam Wangyal

67

Which of these scientists discovered the vaccine for rabies in 1885?

A: Edward Jenner
B: Robert Koch
C: Alexander Fleming
D: Louis Pasteur

68

Which is the only bird that can also fly backwards?

A: Swallow
B: Hummingbird
C: Weaverbird
D: Kingfisher

69

Which of these is a non-metallic solid?

A: Hydrogen
B: Mercury
C: Sulphur
D: Chlorine

70

Where are the headquarters of the Election Commission of India?

A: New Delhi
B: Kolkata
C: Chennai
D: Hyderabad

If you would like to use your 50:50 please turn to page 209
If you would like to Ask The Audience please turn to page 221
Turn to the answer section on page 231 to find out if you've won ₹80,000

71

In which part of the body would you find the vertebrae?

A: Skull
B: Backbone
C: Femur
D: Ribs

72

How do we better know the Russian revolutionary Vladimir Ilych Ulyanov?

A: Stalin
B: Lenin
C: Trotsky
D: Mayakovsky

73

Vamana is the avatar of which Hindu deity?

A: Brahma
B: Vishnu
C: Shiva
D: Indra

74

Which of the following locations has not been a battlefield?

A: Panipat
B: Plassey
C: Buxar
D: Lumbini

75

Who among these was never a President of the Congress (I)?

A: Indira Gandhi
B: Rajiv Gandhi
C: Sanjay Gandhi
D: Sonia Gandhi

If you would like to use your 50:50 please turn to page 209
If you would like to Ask The Audience please turn to page 221
Turn to the answer section on page 231 to find out if you've won ₹80,000

76

What metal is extracted from bauxite?

A: Iron
B: Steel
C: Copper
D: Aluminium

77

Who said "That's one small step for man, one giant leap for mankind"?

A: Edwin Aldrin
B: Edmund Hillary
C: Richard Nixon
D: Neil Armstrong

78

The Buddhist missionary Sanghamitra was the daughter of which ruler?

A: Chandragupta
B: Ashoka
C: Bindusara
D: Dasharatha

79

Which of these diseases is caused by a virus?

A: Cholera
B: Typhoid
C: Leprosy
D: Influenza

80

Which actor's real name was Harihar Jariwala?

A: Jagdeep
B: Jeetendra
C: Sanjeev Kumar
D: Raaj Kumar

If you would like to use your 50:50 please turn to page 209
If you would like to Ask The Audience please turn to page 221
Turn to the answer section on page 231 to find out if you've won ₹80,000

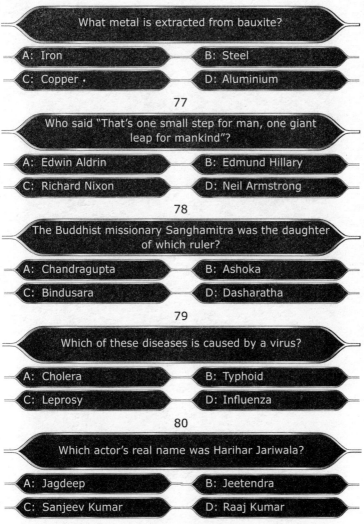

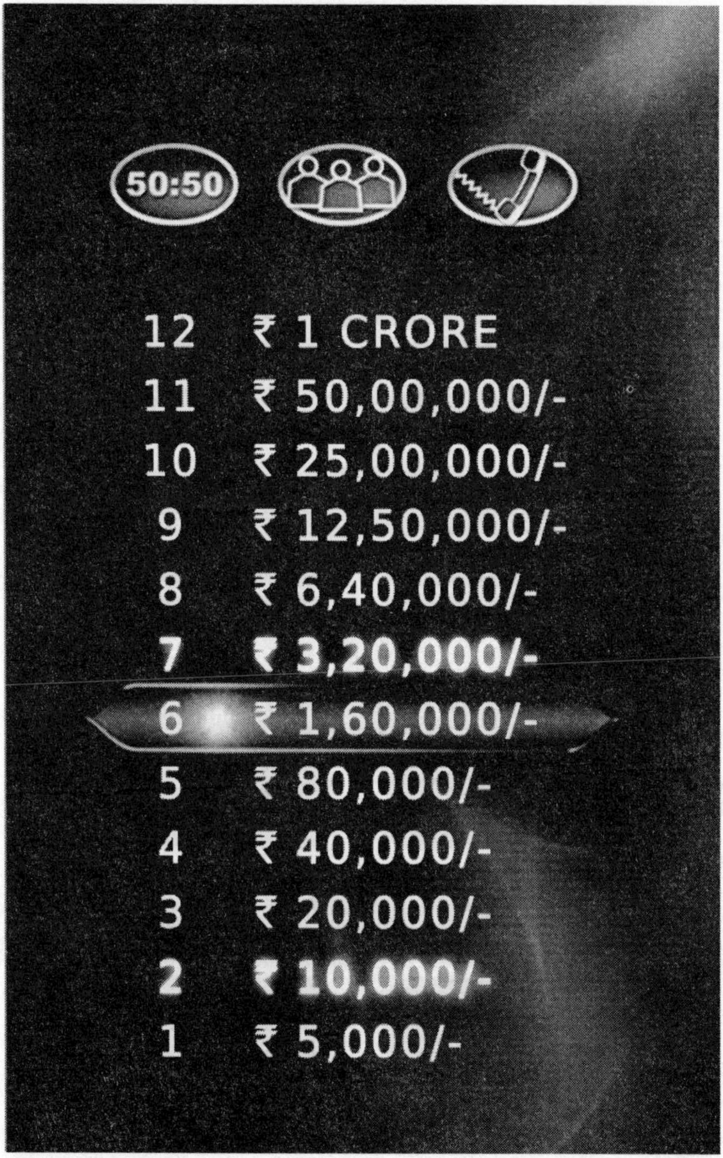
50:50
12 ₹ 1 CRORE
11 ₹ 50,00,000/-
10 ₹ 25,00,000/-
9 ₹ 12,50,000/-
8 ₹ 6,40,000/-
7 ₹ 3,20,000/-
6 ₹ 1,60,000/-
5 ₹ 80,000/-
4 ₹ 40,000/-
3 ₹ 20,000/-
2 ₹ 10,000/-
1 ₹ 5,000/-

6 ♦ ₹1,60,000

1

The emblem for RK Films was taken from an image from which of these films?

A: Awara
B: Barsaat
C: Shree 420
D: Jagte Raho

2

Which of these types of sarees would you associate with Gujarat?

A: Maheshwari
B: Patola
C: Chanderi
D: Paithani

3

Which Asian country's flag bears peepal leaves?

A: Nepal
B: Bhutan
C: Sri Lanka
D: Thailand

4

Which calendar names successive years after 12 animals?

A: Saka
B: Chinese
C: Gregorian
D: Hebrew

5

Which of these batsmen had an average of 99.94 runs in Test cricket?

A: Gary Sobers
B: Don Bradman
C: Sunil Gavaskar
D: George Headley

If you would like to use your 50:50 please turn to page 209
If you would like to Ask The Audience please turn to page 221
Turn to the answer section on page 231 to find out if you've won ₹1,60,000

6

Who wrote 'Ritusamhara'?

A: Surdas
B: Tulsidas
C: Kalidas
D: Ramdas

7

Which of these temples is in Tamil Nadu?

A: Lingaraj Temple
B: Dilwara Temples
C: Somnath Temple
D: Meenakshi Temple

8

To which of these categories do lac-producing creatures belong?

A: Animals
B: Birds
C: Insects
D: Fishes

9

Who played Kasturba in Richard Attenborough's film 'Gandhi'?

A: Rohini Hattangadi
B: Pallavi Joshi
C: Anita Kanwar
D: Neena Gupta

10

Which of these Sufi saints is buried in Delhi?

A: Moinuddin Chishti
B: Salim Chishti
C: Haji Ali
D: Nizamuddin Auliya

If you would like to use your 50:50 please turn to page 209
If you would like to Ask The Audience please turn to page 221
Turn to the answer section on page 231 to find out if you've won ₹1,60,000

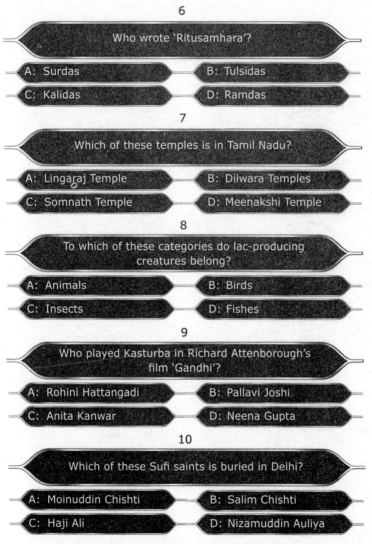

11

After which festival is 'Hola Mohalla' observed in Punjab?

A: Diwali
B: Baisakhi
C: Holi
D: Lohri

12

Raja Sawai Jai Singh was the ruler of which place?

A: Jodhpur
B: Sawai Madhopur
C: Ajmer
D: Amber

13

On the banks of which river is Madurai situated?

A: Krishna
B: Kaveri
C: Vaigai
D: Wainganga

14

Which of these names means 'air'?

A: Sushil
B: Pankaj
C: Neeraj
D: Samir

15

Without whose consent can a bill passed by Parliament not be law in India?

A: Prime Minister
B: President
C: Attorney General
D: Vice President

If you would like to use your 50:50 please turn to page 209
If you would like to Ask The Audience please turn to page 221
Turn to the answer section on page 231 to find out if you've won ₹1,60,000

16

Which planet's largest satellite is the Titan?

A: Saturn
B: Jupiter
C: Uranus
D: Venus

17

Who among these has never been a nominated member of the Rajya Sabha?

A: Jaya Bachchan
B: Hema Malini
C: Amitabh Bachchan
D: Shabana Azmi

18

According to the Mahabharata, out of what was Brahma born?

A: Vishnu's navel
B: Shiva's hair
C: Vishnu's feet
D: Durga's third eye

19

Which of these is not the name of a news agency in India?

A: PTI
B: UNI
C: Samachar Bharati
D: UTI

20

In which modern country would you find Genghis Khan's birthplace?

A: Kyrgyzstan
B: Mongolia
C: Tajikistan
D: Kazakhstan

If you would like to use your 50:50 please turn to page 209
If you would like to Ask The Audience please turn to page 221
Turn to the answer section on page 231 to find out if you've won ₹1,60,000

21

Which Indian mammal is found in 'clouded' and 'snow' varieties?

A: Lion

B: Yak

C: Leopard

D: Deer

22

Which cartoon strip by R K Laxman represented the antics of 'The Common Man'?

A: Business As Usual

B: Here and Now

C: You Said It

D: Double Talk

23

Who was the Indian Union Defence Minister during the Indo-Pak war of 1971?

A: Jagjivan Ram

B: Indira Gandhi

C: C Subramaniam

D: Y B Chavan

24

Which novel tells the story of 1001 gifted children born on 15 August 1947?

A: Heat and Dust

B: In a Free State

C: God of Small Things

D: Midnight's Children

25

Which two countries fought the first Opium War in the nineteenth century?

A: Britain and China

B: Russia and China

C: Britain and Japan

D: China and Japan

If you would like to use your 50:50 please turn to page 209
If you would like to Ask The Audience please turn to page 221
Turn to the answer section on page 231 to find out if you've won ₹1,60,000

26

Which of these present day cities was named after the founder of the Tata empire?

A: Bhilai

B: Bokaro

C: Jamshedpur

D: Jamnagar

27

Which of these literary works was not written by Tulsidas?

A: Ramcharitamanas

B: Vinay Patrika

C: Geet Govinda

D: Kavitawali

28

What are Jaguar, Mirage and MiG names of?

A: Nuclear Missiles

B: Submarines

C: Aircrafts

D: Rocket Launchers

29

Which avatar of Vishnu killed Hiranyakasipu?

A: Kurma

B: Varaha

C: Vamana

D: Narasimha

30

Over which of these territories did the French rule till 1951?

A: Goa

B: Chandernagore

C: Lakshadweep

D: Daman & Diu

If you would like to use your 50:50 please turn to page 209
If you would like to Ask The Audience please turn to page 221
Turn to the answer section on page 231 to find out if you've won ₹1,60,000

31

Which Lodi Sultan was defeated at Panipat by Babur?

A: Sikandar Lodi
B: Tardi Beg
C: Ibrahim Lodi
D: Sher Shah Suri

32

Which of the following diseases is not caused by bacteria?

A: Leprosy
B: Tuberculosis
C: Typhoid
D: Chicken Pox

33

From which language has the word 'halwa' been derived?

A: Punjabi
B: Arabic
C: Hindi
D: Portuguese

34

Where is Jhumri Talaiya, a place famous among listeners of Vividh Bharati?

A: Uttar Pradesh
B: Bihar
C: Chhattisgarh
D: Jharkhand

35

With which sport are the Thomas Cup and Uber Cup associated?

A: Tennis
B: Badminton
C: Table Tennis
D: Squash

If you would like to use your 50:50 please turn to page 209
If you would like to Ask The Audience please turn to page 221
Turn to the answer section on page 231 to find out if you've won ₹1,60,000

36

Which of these is the tomb of Mohammad Adil Shah of Bijapur?

A: Golghar

B: Haji Ali

C: Daria Daulat Bagh

D: Gol Gumbaz

37

What was the actor Guru Dutt's surname?

A: Dutt

B: Padukone

C: Reddy

D: Bhonsle

38

The lack of which of these causes osteoporosis?

A: Potassium

B: Sodium

C: Sulphur

D: Calcium

39

Who among these scored a century at Lord's on his test debut?

A: Sachin Tendulkar

B: Sourav Ganguly

C: Rahul Dravid

D: Virender Sehwag

40

When was 'Jana Gana Mana' officially adopted as our National Anthem?

A: 1950

B: 1947

C: 1952

D: 1948

If you would like to use your 50:50 please turn to page 209
If you would like to Ask The Audience please turn to page 221
Turn to the answer section on page 231 to find out if you've won ₹1,60,000

41

Which capital city do Heathrow and Gatwick airports serve?

A: London
B: Canberra
C: Washington DC
D: Dublin

42

Which of these is not a billiards player?

A: Wilson Jones
B: Michael Ferreira
C: Geet Sethi
D: Jaspal Rana

43

Which Arab country fought a war with Iran from 1980 to 1988?

A: Saudi Arabia
B: Libya
C: Jordan
D: Iraq

44

Which of these rivers was named after the Sanskrit word 'Sindhu'?

A: Narmada
B: Indus
C: Ganga
D: Brahmaputra

45

What is the 'Jaipur foot'?

A: A Toy
B: A Disease
C: An Artificial Limb
D: An Army Regiment

If you would like to use your 50:50 please turn to page 209
If you would like to Ask The Audience please turn to page 221
Turn to the answer section on page 231 to find out if you've won ₹1,60,000

46

In which sport is the 'pen-holder grip' used?

A: Table Tennis
B: Badminton
C: Tennis
D: Squash

47

Which planet approaches the closest to Earth during its revolution?

A: Venus
B: Mars
C: Mercury
D: Jupiter

48

Where is the National Defence Academy located?

A: Dehradun
B: Chennai
C: New Delhi
D: Khadakwasla

49

What kind of creature is 'salmonella'?

A: Virus
B: Fish
C: Bacterium
D: Blood platelet

50

In which region did the Palas rule between the 8th and the 12th centuries?

A: Kashmir
B: Bengal
C: Gujarat
D: Rajasthan

If you would like to use your 50:50 please turn to page 210
If you would like to Ask The Audience please turn to page 222
Turn to the answer section on page 231 to find out if you've won ₹1,60,000

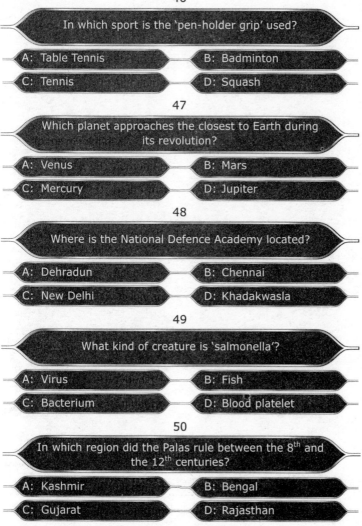

51

Which of these novels was written by Mulk Raj Anand?

A: The Guide
B: My Days
C: Coolie
D: The Blue Umbrella

52

Which of these films won a record 11 Oscars?

A: Gandhi
B: The Hurt Locker
C: Schindler's List
D: Titanic

53

Which Indian cricketer was nicknamed 'Colonel'?

A: C.K. Nayudu
B: Sandeep Patil
C: Dilip Vengsarkar
D: Kirti Azad

54

Which of these is a ball-and-socket joint?

A: Neck
B: Elbow
C: Shoulder
D: Wrist

55

How do we now know the General Purpose vehicle developed during World War II?

A: Truck
B: Jeep
C: Chopper
D: Van

If you would like to use your 50:50 please turn to page 210
If you would like to Ask The Audience please turn to page 222
Turn to the answer section on page 231 to find out if you've won ₹1,60,000

56

Which ruler did Qutub-ud-din Aibak serve before he became a king?

A: Mahmud of Ghazni
B: Mohammad Ghori
C: Mahmud Gawan
D: Muhammad Shaibani

57

Which Hindi film actress was originally named Mahjabeen?

A: Meena Kumari
B: Madhubala
C: Waheeda Rehman
D: Mumtaz

58

Which socio-religious organisation's slogan is 'Back to the Vedas'?

A: Arya Samaj
B: VHP
C: Shiv Sena
D: ISKCON

59

What liquid is usually present in a medicinal solution known as a tincture?

A: Water
B: Mercury
C: Formaldehyde
D: Alcohol

60

In which city is the Chinnaswamy Stadium situated?

A: Hyderabad
B: Bangalore
C: Chennai
D: Thiruvananthapuram

If you would like to use your 50:50 please turn to page 210
If you would like to Ask The Audience please turn to page 222
Turn to the answer section on page 231 to find out if you've won ₹1,60,000

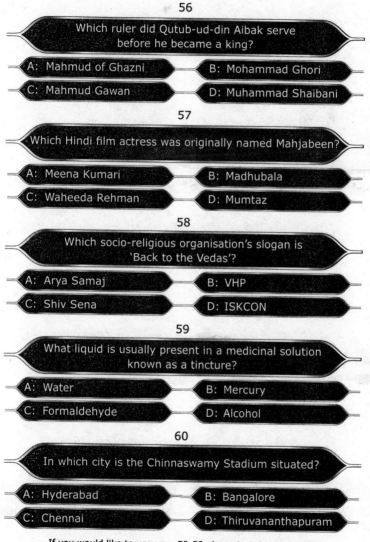

61

Who learnt archery using a clay statue of Dronacharya as his guru?

A: Karna

B: Abhimanyu

C: Ashwatthama

D: Eklavya

62

Which of the following belongs to the ginger family?

A: Turmeric

B: Asafoetida

C: Saffron

D: Nutmeg

63

Which of these national parks is in the state of Uttarakhand?

A: Gir

B: Nandan Kanan

C: Corbett

D: Kaziranga

64

What is an AK-47?

A: Flintlock Rifle

B: Assault Rifle

C: Musket

D: Carbine

65

Where is the Mughal Emperor Akbar's mausoleum located?

A: Agra

B: Sikandra

C: Fatehpur Sikri

D: Bulandshahr

If you would like to use your 50:50 please turn to page 210
If you would like to Ask The Audience please turn to page 222
Turn to the answer section on page 231 to find out if you've won ₹1,60,000

66

Which of these sportspersons has won an Olympic Gold medal?

A: Sushil Kumar
B: Leander Paes
C: Abhinav Bindra
D: Karnam Malleswari

67

With which Indian language is 'Sangam Literature' associated?

A: Telugu
B: Marathi
C: Tamil
D: Bengali

68

Yehudi Menuhin was a world renowned exponent of which musical instrument?

A: Sitar
B: Violin
C: Piano
D: Guitar

69

What are Kakori, Shashlik and Husseini types of?

A: Kebabs
B: Face Masks
C: Painting styles
D: Mountain Peaks

70

With which of these would you associate the Richter and Mercalli scales?

A: Flood
B: Earthquake
C: Rain
D: Typhoon

If you would like to use your 50:50 please turn to page 210
If you would like to Ask The Audience please turn to page 222
Turn to the answer section on page 231 to find out if you've won ₹1,60,000

71

Which Mughal Emperor's court poet was Mirza Ghalib?

A: Akbar
B: Jahangir
C: Shah Jahan
D: Bahadur Shah II

72

Which of these countries has not had a Prime Minister of Indian origin?

A: Fiji
B: Singapore
C: Mauritius
D: Guyana

73

What does the 'X' stand for in the term X-ray?

A: Exact
B: Unknown
C: Electric
D: Ultraviolet

74

In which state is the famous battlefield of Plassey located?

A: Jharkhand
B: Bihar
C: West Bengal
D: Chhattisgarh

75

Which country has a national airlines called Garuda?

A: Sri Lanka
B: Nepal
C: Cambodia
D: Indonesia

If you would like to use your 50:50 please turn to page 210
If you would like to Ask The Audience please turn to page 222
Turn to the answer section on page 231 to find out if you've won ₹1,60,000

76

What was the name of Mahatma Gandhi's father?

A: Madan Chand
B: Gopal Krishna
C: Dharam Chand
D: Karamchand

77

Which of these metals is found in both bronze and brass?

A: Silver
B: Copper
C: Tin
D: Iron

78

To whom is the Sankatamochan temple in Varanasi dedicated?

A: Hanuman
B: Ganesha
C: Krishna
D: Rama

79

Which title is usually held by the eldest son of the British monarch?

A: Duke of Edinburgh
B: Prince of Wales
C: Grand Prince
D: Duke of York

80

Which of these personalities was born in India?

A: Mother Teresa
B: Bhikaiji Cama
C: Sonia Gandhi
D: Annie Besant

If you would like to use your 50:50 please turn to page 210
If you would like to Ask The Audience please turn to page 222
Turn to the answer section on page 231 to find out if you've won ₹1,60,000

[illegible]

30

[illegible]

If you would like to [illegible] please turn to page [illegible]
If you would like to Ask The Audience please turn to page [illegible]
Turn to the answer section on page [illegible] to find out if you've won [illegible]

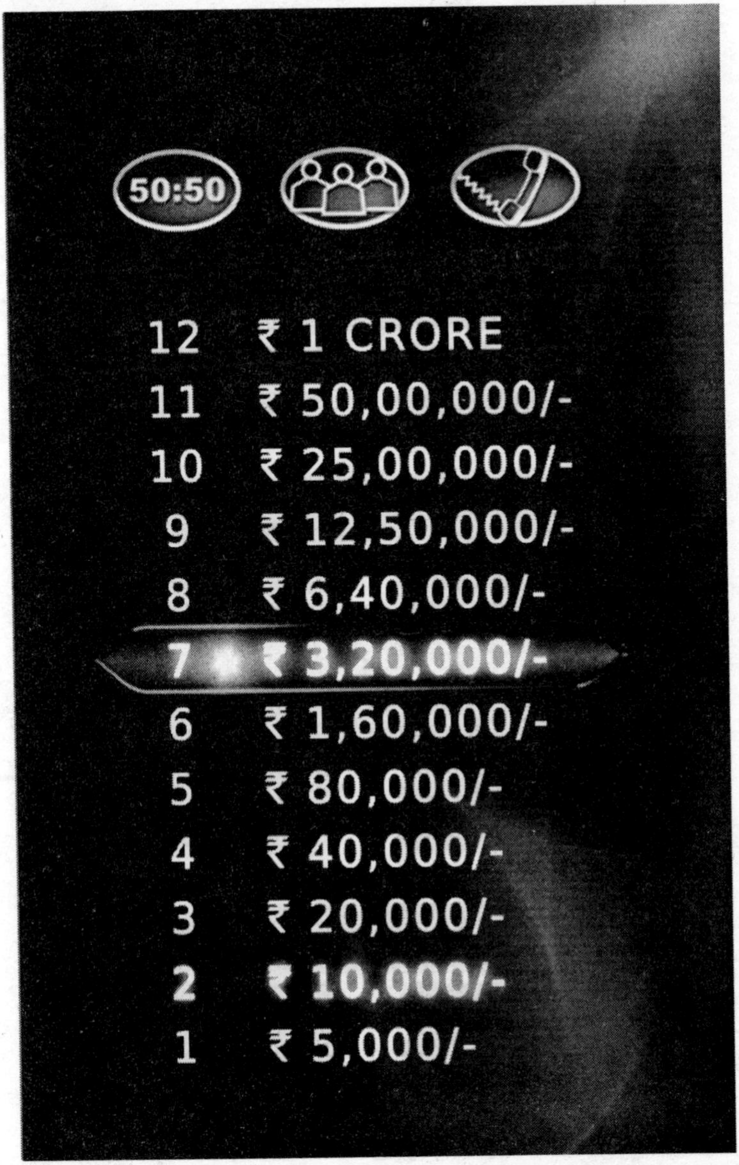

50:50
12 ₹ 1 CRORE
11 ₹ 50,00,000/-
10 ₹ 25,00,000/-
9 ₹ 12,50,000/-
8 ₹ 6,40,000/-
7 ₹ 3,20,000/-
6 ₹ 1,60,000/-
5 ₹ 80,000/-
4 ₹ 40,000/-
3 ₹ 20,000/-
2 ₹ 10,000/-
1 ₹ 5,000/-

7 ✦ ₹ 3,20,000

1

In which mountain range does the Siachen glacier lie?

A: Himalaya
B: Karakoram
C: Kunlun Shan
D: Hindu Kush

2

Aboard which space shuttle did Kalpana Chawla go into space?

A: Discovery
B: Endeavour
C: Atlantis
D: Columbia

3

What is the currency of Afghanistan?

A: Riyal
B: Afghani
C: Dirham
D: Rupiah

4

For which sport is the Rangaswami Cup awarded?

A: Badminton
B: Football
C: Hockey
D: Table Tennis

5

Which dynasty ruled Delhi immediately after the Tughlaqs?

A: Sayyid
B: Lodi
C: Mughal
D: Khilji

If you would like to use your 50:50 please turn to page 210
If you would like to Ask The Audience please turn to page 222
Turn to the answer section on page 231 to find out if you've won ₹3,20,000

6

Which chemical compound in tea is responsible for its stimulating effect?

A: Carmine
B: Caffeine
C: Nicotine
D: Tannin

7

What is the minimum age to be eligible for election as President of India?

A: 25 years
B: 30 years
C: 35 years
D: 50 years

8

Which is the first month of the Islamic calendar?

A: Ashura
B: Muharram
C: Ramadan
D: Hadith

9

In Australia, what are MCG and SCG names of?

A: Anabolic Steroids
B: Cricket Stadiums
C: Kangaroo Parks
D: Rock Bands

10

In Hindu tradition, on which serpent does Vishnu recline?

A: Takshaka
B: Karkotaka
C: Dhritarashtra
D: Adi Sesha

If you would like to use your 50:50 please turn to page 210
If you would like to Ask The Audience please turn to page 222
Turn to the answer section on page 231 to find out if you've won ₹3,20,000

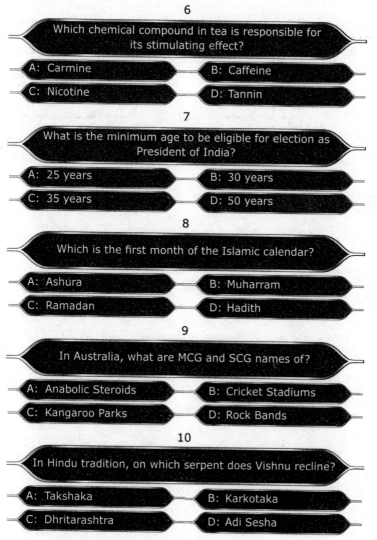

11

Whom did Sonia Gandhi succeed as the President of the Congress in 1998?

A: P V Narasimha Rao
B: Pranab Mukherjee
C: Sitaram Kesri
D: Sharad Pawar

12

Which of these hill stations is located in the Palani Hills?

A: Mount Abu
B: Darjeeling
C: Kodaikanal
D: Mahabaleshwar

13

Which Hindi film comedian's real name is Badruddin Jamaluddin Qazi?

A: Mehmood
B: Jalal Agha
C: Johnny Walker
D: Ajit

14

In which city was Gandhiji on the day of India's Independence?

A: Lahore
B: Madras
C: Bombay
D: Calcutta

15

In which yug was Lord Krishna born?

A: Kaliyug
B: Dwaparyug
C: Satyug
D: Tretayug

If you would like to use your 50:50 please turn to page 210
If you would like to Ask The Audience please turn to page 222
Turn to the answer section on page 231 to find out if you've won ₹3,20,000

16

Which of these sportspersons of Indian origin is not a Test cricketer?

A: Sonny Ramadhin
B: Rohan Kanhai
C: Dipak Patel
D: Vijay Singh

17

A surprise attack on which of these led to USA joining World War II?

A: Gold Coast
B: Diamond Harbour
C: Ivory Coast
D: Pearl Harbour

18

According to the Constitution of India, who can dissolve the Lok Sabha?

A: Prime Minister
B: Lok Sabha Speaker
C: Attorney General
D: President

19

According to Hindu mythology, which of these demons causes all eclipses?

A: Bali
B: Kumbha
C: Rahu
D: Kesi

20

Which Mughal Emperor struck leather coins after a bhishti saved his life?

A: Akbar
B: Humayun
C: Babur
D: Aurangzeb

If you would like to use your 50:50 please turn to page 210
If you would like to Ask The Audience please turn to page 222
Turn to the answer section on page 231 to find out if you've won ₹3,20,000

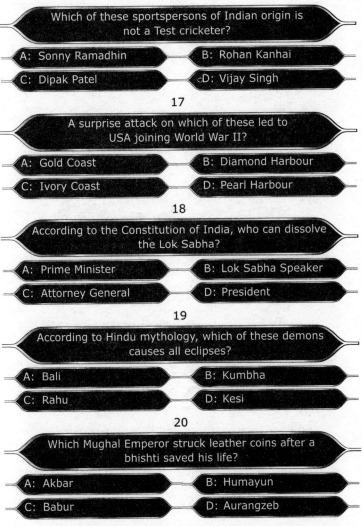

21

In which of these sports does a player need to win at least 11 points to win a game?

A: Tennis
B: Basketball
C: Table Tennis
D: Netball

22

Which of these Japanese words is a war cry?

A: Bonsai
B: Banzai
C: Sensei
D: Nikkei

23

In the Ramayana, where did Bharata worship the 'khadau' or sandals of Rama?

A: Nandigrama
B: Ekchakra
C: Chitrakoot
D: Panchavati

24

Kalhana's 'Rajatarangini' chronicles the history of which place in India?

A: Mewar
B: Kashmir
C: Bengal
D: Awadh

25

The underwater 'Channel Tunnel' connects England with which other country?

A: France
B: Greece
C: Germany
D: Italy

If you would like to use your 50:50 please turn to page 210
If you would like to Ask The Audience please turn to page 222
Turn to the answer section on page 231 to find out if you've won ₹3,20,000

26

Raja and Radha Reddy are renowned exponents of which classical dance form?

A: Bharatnatyam
B: Kathak
C: Kuchipudi
D: Kathakali

27

Which of these feeds almost exclusively on snakes?

A: Gharial
B: King Cobra
C: Golden Eagle
D: Python

28

Which is India's longest national highway?

A: NH-47
B: NH-3
C: NH-2
D: NH-7

29

Who was the eldest son of the Mughal Emperor Shah Jahan?

A: Aurangzeb
B: Shuja
C: Murad
D: Dara Shikoh

30

With how many countries does India share a land border?

A: Seven
B: Nine
C: Eight
D: Six

If you would like to use your 50:50 please turn to page 210
If you would like to Ask The Audience please turn to page 222
Turn to the answer section on page 231 to find out if you've won ₹3,20,000

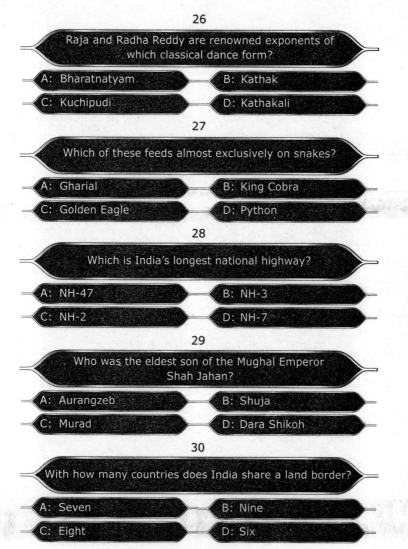

31

Which of these kingdoms was established by Rao Bika in 1488?

A: Jodhpur
B: Bikaner
C: Bhithor
D: Bahawalpur

32

Who is the youngest to score a century in Test cricket?

A: Mohammad Ashraful
B: Shahid Afridi
C: Hasan Raza
D: Mushtaq Mohammad

33

Which of these holy books has 114 chapters called 'Surahs'?

A: Guru Granth Sahib
B: Rig Veda
C: Quran
D: Torah

34

Which of these organs has no known function?

A: Pancreas
B: Appendix
C: Liver
D: Spleen

35

What is the capital of the United Arab Emirates?

A: Abu Dhabi
B: Sharjah
C: Dubai
D: Fujairah

If you would like to use your 50:50 please turn to page 210
If you would like to Ask The Audience please turn to page 222
Turn to the answer section on page 231 to find out if you've won ₹3,20,000

36

At which Congress session was the Quit India resolution passed in 1942?

A: Calcutta
B: Bombay
C: Madras
D: Nagpur

37

Which of these beaches is not in Chennai?

A: Elliots
B: Santhome
C: Anjuna
D: Marina

38

Which of these is not an Olympic event for women?

A: Pole Vault
B: 4 x 400 m Relay
C: 50 km Walk
D: Triple Jump

39

Which state was known as Gauda in ancient India?

A: Bengal
B: Assam
C: Orissa
D: Bihar

40

The 'Himalayan' and 'Nilgiri' are the wild varieties of which animal?

A: Goat
B: Deer
C: Rabbit
D: Cat

If you would like to use your 50:50 please turn to page 210
If you would like to Ask The Audience please turn to page 222
Turn to the answer section on page 231 to find out if you've won ₹3,20,000

41

Which popular pilgrimage spot in South India is set among Saptagiri hills?

A: Madurai
B: Udupi
C: Tirupati
D: Chidambaram

42

Which ruler of the Lodi dynasty founded the city of Agra?

A: Sikandar Lodi
B: Bahlol Lodi
C: Ibrahim Lodi
D: Daulat Khan Lodi

43

What were the names of the oxen in Premchand's story 'Do Bailon Ki Kathha'?

A: Heera-Moti
B: Badal-Rustam
C: Laloo-Kaloo
D: Sohni-Mahiwal

44

What is the name of the mat on which judo matches are held?

A: Ippon
B: Tatami
C: Katsu
D: Roppongi

45

Which king is associated with the legendary Rani Roopmati of Mandu?

A: Hyder Ali
B: Baz Bahadur
C: Man Singh
D: Allauddin Khilji

If you would like to use your 50:50 please turn to page 210
If you would like to Ask The Audience please turn to page 222
Turn to the answer section on page 231 to find out if you've won ₹3,20,000

46

By picking up what did Gandhiji break an unjust law on 6 April 1930?

A: Cotton
B: Indigo
C: Salt
D: Silk

47

Which team did Raj Singh Dungarpur captain in the Ranji Trophy tournament?

A: Rajasthan
B: Vidarbha
C: Madhya Pradesh
D: Baroda

48

Who played the role of the 'Sahib' in the classic 'Sahib, Bibi aur Ghulam'?

A: Sapru
B: Nasir Hussain
C: Rehman
D: Guru Dutt

49

Where was Chanakya educated?

A: Nalanda
B: Taxila
C: Ujjain
D: Vikramshila

50

In Hindustani classical music, how many matras are there in the 'teen tal'?

A: Three
B: Six
C: Sixteen
D: Twelve

If you would like to use your 50:50 please turn to page 211
If you would like to Ask The Audience please turn to page 223
Turn to the answer section on page 231 to find out if you've won ₹3,20,000

51

Who wrote one of the most complete accounts of ancient India, 'Indica'?

A: Megasthenes
B: Marco Polo
C: Nicolo Conti
D: Seleucus Nicator

52

Which Sikh guru built the Akal Takht?

A: Guru Arjan Dev
B: Guru Hargobind
C: Guru Gobind Singh
D: Guru Tegh Bahadur

53

Which is the governing body for international hockey?

A: FIDE
B: FIFA
C: ICC
D: FIH

54

What is the freezing point of water on the Fahrenheit scale?

A: 100 degrees
B: -273 degrees
C: 32 degrees
D: 0 degree

55

In Hindu tradition, which of these is not one of the 'Panchatatva'?

A: Sameer
B: Akshata
C: Gagan
D: Agni

If you would like to use your 50:50 please turn to page 211
If you would like to Ask The Audience please turn to page 223
Turn to the answer section on page 231 to find out if you've won ₹3,20,000

56

To go to which of these hill stations would you take a flight to Bagdogra?

A: Simla
B: Mt Abu
C: Ooty
D: Darjeeling

57

Which of these films is not based on a story by Munshi Premchand?

A: Sadgati
B: Mazdoor
C: Godan
D: Gaman

58

According to WHO, which of these diseases has been completely eradicated?

A: Chicken Pox
B: Tuberculosis
C: Small Pox
D: Influenza

59

In which of these events would an athlete run in the 'exchange zone'?

A: Pole Vault
B: Long Jump
C: Relay Race
D: Steeplechase

60

Mont Blanc is the highest peak of which mountain range?

A: Alps
B: Andes
C: Atlas
D: Rockies

If you would like to use your 50:50 please turn to page 211
If you would like to Ask The Audience please turn to page 223
Turn to the answer section on page 232 to find out if you've won ₹3,20,000

61

The introduction of a new version of what sparked off the uprising of 1857?

A: Bread
B: Belt
C: Rifle
D: Shoes

62

Which of these is an infection and not a parasite?

A: Hookworm
B: Roundworm
C: Ringworm
D: Tapeworm

63

Normally what is the voltage of dry battery cells, also called pencil cells?

A: 10 volts
B: 1.5 volts
C: 5 volts
D: 220 volts

64

What are suspension, arch, girder and cantilever types of?

A: Bridges
B: Dams
C: Cranes
D: Trucks

65

Who founded the city of Hyderabad?

A: Qutub-ud-din Aibak
B: Quli Qutub Shah
C: Bahman Shah
D: Hyder Ali

If you would like to use your 50:50 please turn to page 211
If you would like to Ask The Audience please turn to page 223
Turn to the answer section on page 232 to find out if you've won ₹3,20,000

66

In which mountain range does Mt. Abu lie?

A: Satpuras

B: Shivaliks

C: Aravalis

D: Vindhyas

67

The Victoria Cross is the highest military decoration of which country?

A: USA

B: Russia

C: Japan

D: Great Britain

68

What are the chief components of proteins?

A: Amino acids

B: Citric acid

C: Acetic acid

D: Lactic acid

69

Which Indian ruler sent a Buddhist missionary to Ceylon in 251 BC?

A: Chandragupta II

B: Bimbisara

C: Ashoka

D: Ajatshatru

70

Which of these is a tribal district in Gujarat?

A: Gonds

B: Dangs

C: Gaddis

D: Khonds

If you would like to use your 50:50 please turn to page 211
If you would like to Ask The Audience please turn to page 223
Turn to the answer section on page 232 to find out if you've won ₹3,20,000

71

In Hindu mythology, who among the following was not killed by Krishna?

A: Pootna
B: Kansa
C: Jarasandha
D: Shishupala

72

Which animal gets its name from the Greek words for 'nose horn'?

A: Unicorn
B: Rhinoceros
C: Tapir
D: Diplodocus

73

When was the Indian Parliament first constituted?

A: 1947
B: 1952
C: 1950
D: 1954

74

On which of these scales are acidity and alkalinity measured?

A: Moh's scale
B: Richter scale
C: pH scale
D: Mercalli scale

75

What award does the highest goal scorer in the FIFA World Cup get?

A: Golden Glove
B: Golden Boot
C: Fair Play Trophy
D: Golden Ball

If you would like to use your 50:50 please turn to page 211
If you would like to Ask The Audience please turn to page 223
Turn to the answer section on page 232 to find out if you've won ₹3,20,000

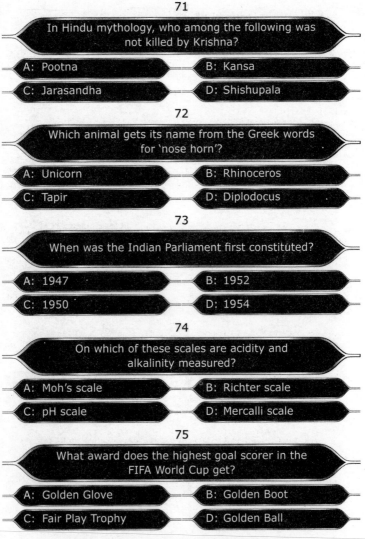

76

Which Maratha queen's capital was Maheshwar?

A: Lakshmibai

B: Ahilyabai Holkar

C: Jijabai

D: Chand Bibi

77

Which of these states of Australia is an island?

A: Queensland

B: Tasmania

C: Victoria

D: New South Wales

78

Who is the author of the book 'India Wins Freedom'?

A: Abul Kalam Azad

B: Mahatma Gandhi

C: Rajendra Prasad

D: S Radhakrishnan

79

What nickname was given to Arjuna because he was ambidextrous?

A: Iravan

B: Kiriti

C: Sabyasachi

D: Shuk

80

Against which country did Anil Kumble take 10 wickets in a test innings?

A: Australia

B: Sri Lanka

C: South Africa

D: Pakistan

If you would like to use your 50:50 please turn to page 211
If you would like to Ask The Audience please turn to page 223
Turn to the answer section on page 232 to find out if you've won ₹3,20,000

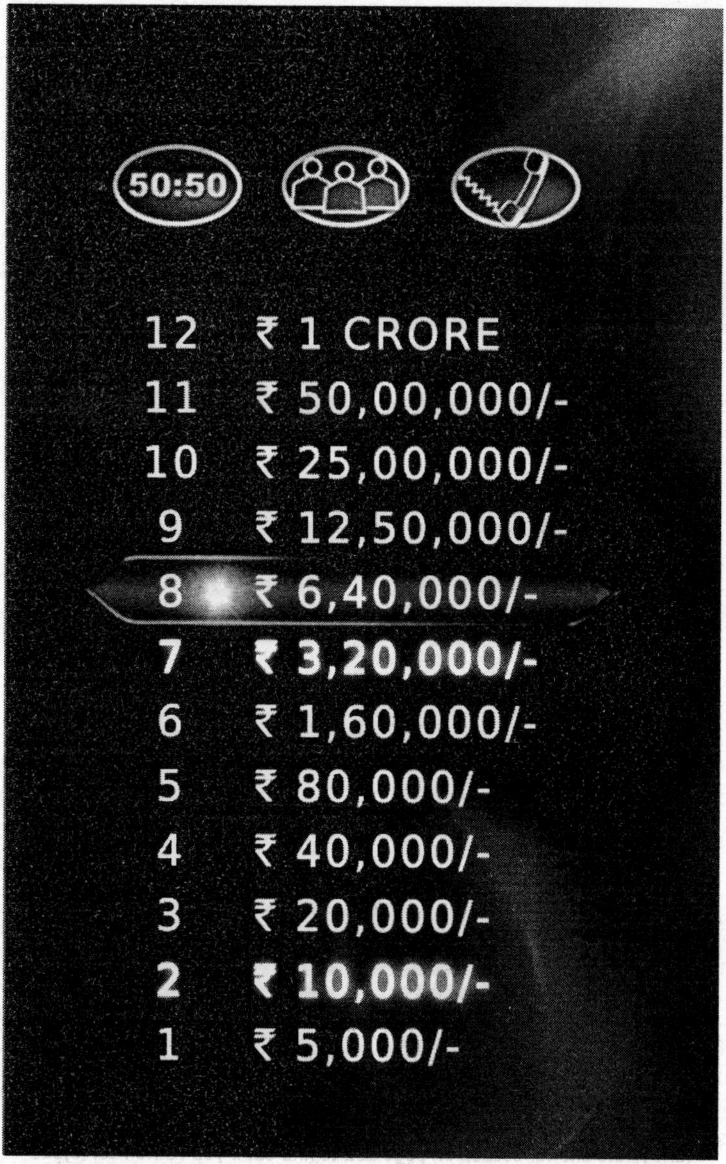
50:50
12 ₹ 1 CRORE
11 ₹ 50,00,000/-
10 ₹ 25,00,000/-
9 ₹ 12,50,000/-
8 ₹ 6,40,000/-
7 ₹ 3,20,000/-
6 ₹ 1,60,000/-
5 ₹ 80,000/-
4 ₹ 40,000/-
3 ₹ 20,000/-
2 ₹ 10,000/-
1 ₹ 5,000/-

8 ◆ ₹6,40,000

1

In Olympic archery, what is the colour of the central ring of the target?

A: White

B: Red

C: Yellow

D: Black

2

Which film featured the song 'Hawa mein udta jaaye mera laal dupatta...'?

A: Sangam

B: Barsaat

C: Awara

D: Shree 420

3

How many languages are listed in the 8th Schedule of the Indian Constitution?

A: Twelve

B: Fifteen

C: Twenty-two

D: Twenty-one

4

Which planet rotates fastest on its axis?

A: Mercury

B: Pluto

C: Jupiter

D: Saturn

5

Which gulf will one have to cross to get to Diu from Daman?

A: Gulf of Kutch

B: Gulf of Mannar

C: Gulf of Martaban

D: Gulf of Khambhat

If you would like to use your 50:50 please turn to page 211
If you would like to Ask The Audience please turn to page 223
Turn to the answer section on page 232 to find out if you've won ₹6,40,000

6

In which script is English written?

A: Roman
B: Greek
C: Cyrillic
D: Hebrew

7

Where are the headquarters of OPEC?

A: Tehran
B: Riyadh
C: Vienna
D: Geneva

8

After which Prime Minister has an item of clothing been named?

A: Manmohan Singh
B: Indira Gandhi
C: Jawaharlal Nehru
D: Charan Singh

9

Who was the last Jain Tirthankar?

A: Parshvanath
B: Mahavira
C: Neminath
D: Rishabhdev

10

What does 'Sita' literally mean in Sanskrit?

A: Bucket
B: Soil
C: Furrow
D: Fire

If you would like to use your 50:50 please turn to page 211
If you would like to Ask The Audience please turn to page 223
Turn to the answer section on page 232 to find out if you've won ₹6,40,000

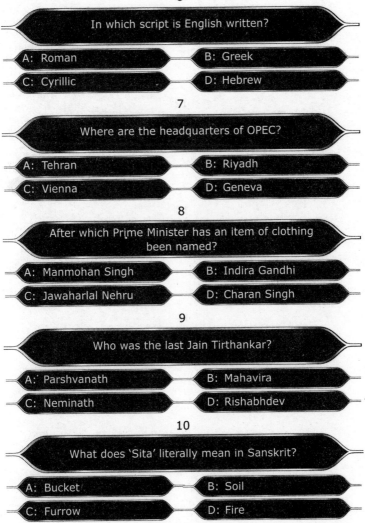

11

On what surface are French Open tennis matches played at the Roland Garros?

A: Grass
B: Synthetic
C: Clay
D: Concrete

12

Which Indian author wrote the novel 'The Financial Expert'?

A: R K Narayan
B: Nirad C Chaudhuri
C: Mulk Raj Anand
D: Rohinton Mistry

13

Which Indian state is a leading producer of saffron?

A: Tamil Nadu
B: Sikkim
C: Himachal Pradesh
D: Jammu & Kashmir

14

What was the original name of Valmiki?

A: Divakar
B: Ravi Das
C: Ratnakar
D: Prabhakar

15

Which Mughal Emperor's father-in-law was Itmad-ud-daulah?

A: Shah Jahan
B: Jahangir
C: Aurangzeb
D: Humayun

If you would like to use your 50:50 please turn to page 211
If you would like to Ask The Audience please turn to page 223
Turn to the answer section on page 232 to find out if you've won ₹6,40,000

16

Lack of iron in the body causes a low level of which substance in blood?

A: Carbon Dioxide
B: Urea
C: Haemoglobin
D: Nitrogen

17

Who is the first Indian cricketer to score a century in Test cricket for India?

A: Vijay Hazare
B: Lala Amarnath
C: Vijay Merchant
D: C K Nayudu

18

Whose samadhi in Ahmedabad is called 'Abhay Ghat'?

A: Sardar Patel
B: C Rajagopalachari
C: Morarji Desai
D: Acharya Kripalani

19

Which Indian State or Union Territory was the last to be liberated from a colonial power?

A: Pondicherry
B: Goa
C: Arunachal Pradesh
D: Sikkim

20

Which of these is not a stock market index?

A: Nikkei
B: Sensex
C: Dow Jones
D: GATT

If you would like to use your 50:50 please turn to page 211
If you would like to Ask The Audience please turn to page 223
Turn to the answer section on page 232 to find out if you've won ₹6,40,000

21

Who was the first US President to visit India?

A: John F Kennedy

B: Dwight Eisenhower

C: Richard Nixon

D: Jimmy Carter

22

Which country helped India to set up a public sector steel plant at Bhilai?

A: USA

B: West Germany

C: USSR

D: UK

23

What was Draupadi's name during the period of hiding of the Pandavas?

A: Sairandhri

B: Satyawati

C: Subhadra

D: Bhanu

24

Which of these places is named after a British Viceroy?

A: Wellington

B: Lansdowne

C: McLeodganj

D: Andrewsganj

25

Who is the author of the novel 'Tamas'?

A: Yashpal

B: Shrilal Shukla

C: Khushwant Singh

D: Bhisham Sahni

If you would like to use your 50:50 please turn to page 211
If you would like to Ask The Audience please turn to page 223
Turn to the answer section on page 232 to find out if you've won ₹6,40,000

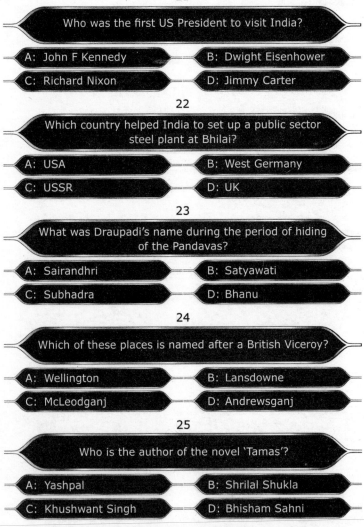

26

Who was the first bowler to cross 500 wickets in Test cricket?

A: Wasim Akram
B: Courtney Walsh
C: Kapil Dev
D: Richard Hadlee

27

Mardana was the devoted Muslim follower of which Sikh guru?

A: Guru Tegh Bahadur
B: Guru Nanak
C: Guru Arjan Dev
D: Guru Gobind Singh

28

Where was the Durand Cup held before the venue was moved to Delhi in 1940?

A: Calcutta
B: Shimla
C: Nainital
D: Bombay

29

In the Mahabharata, who was brought up by Radha and Adhiratha?

A: Shishupala
B: Shikhandi
C: Kirtivarma
D: Karna

30

Who was the first sitting Prime Minister to lose a Lok Sabha election?

A: Jawaharlal Nehru
B: Indira Gandhi
C: Rajiv Gandhi
D: V P Singh

If you would like to use your 50:50 please turn to page 211
If you would like to Ask The Audience please turn to page 223
Turn to the answer section on page 232 to find out if you've won ₹6,40,000

31

According to Hindu mythology, whose son is Narada?

A: Shiva
B: Vishnu
C: Brahma
D: Indra

32

Which of these is not the son of a former Indian Test cricketer?

A: Mohinder Amarnath
B: Rohan Gavaskar
C: Sanjay Manjrekar
D: Sourav Ganguly

33

On the banks of which river is Surat located?

A: Tapti
B: Narmada
C: Sabarmati
D: Mahi

34

Which of these rulers is buried at Sasaram in Bihar?

A: Baz Bahadur
B: Sher Shah Suri
C: Mir Jafar
D: Wajid Ali Shah

35

Which is the longest of the five rivers that together give Punjab its name?

A: Chenab
B: Beas
C: Sutlej
D: Jhelum

If you would like to use your 50:50 please turn to page 211
If you would like to Ask The Audience please turn to page 223
Turn to the answer section on page 232 to find out if you've won ₹6,40,000

36

Which of these countries has never participated in the ICC Cricket World Cup?

A: Canada
B: UAE
C: Holland
D: Malaysia

37

Which of the following Hindi words does not mean 'incomparable'?

A: Anupam
B: Atul
C: Akshay
D: Advitiya

38

Who was Prophet Muhammad's father?

A: Abu Bakr
B: Abdullah
C: Abu Talib
D: Abd al Muttalib

39

In which country is William Shakespeare's play 'Romeo and Juliet' set?

A: England
B: Italy
C: Turkey
D: Russia

40

What does the 'A' stand for in the international news agency, AP?

A: Atlantic
B: Allied
C: Associated
D: Authentic

If you would like to use your 50:50 please turn to page 211
If you would like to Ask The Audience please turn to page 223
Turn to the answer section on page 232 to find out if you've won ₹6,40,000

41

Which of these is not the name of a satellite launched by India?

A: Aryabhatta
B: Bhaskara
C: Dhanwantari
D: Rohini

42

Which leader became the President of his country after 27 years in prison?

A: Yasser Arafat
B: Fidel Castro
C: Nelson Mandela
D: Mujibur Rahman

43

Which is the first letter of the Arabic alphabet?

A: Alfa
B: Alif
C: Olfa
D: Calif

44

Who among these claimed a wicket with his first delivery in Test cricket?

A: Chetan Sharma
B: Shahid Afridi
C: Nilesh Kulkarni
D: Anil Kumble

45

Which of these was Kamsa's sister?

A: Yashodhara
B: Rukmini
C: Devaki
D: Radha

If you would like to use your 50:50 please turn to page 211
If you would like to Ask The Audience please turn to page 223
Turn to the answer section on page 232 to find out if you've won ₹6,40,000

46

In which district of Tamil Nadu is Udhagamandalam situated?

A: Thanjavur
B: Nilgiris
C: Dindigul
D: Erode

47

Which country did the Rana family rule between 1846-1951?

A: Bhutan
B: Sikkim
C: Nepal
D: Burma

48

Who wrote the song 'Aye Mere Vatan Ke Logon', sung by Lata Mangeshkar?

A: Hasrat Jaipuri
B: Kavi Pradeep
C: Bankim Chandra
D: Sahir Ludhianvi

49

Which of these Test cricket grounds is not in India?

A: Green Park
B: Eden Gardens
C: Burlton Park
D: Sabina Park

50

In the Mahabharata, who killed the five sons of Draupadi as they slept?

A: Ashwatthama
B: Duryodhana
C: Laxman Kumar
D: Bhurishravas

If you would like to use your 50:50 please turn to page 212
If you would like to Ask The Audience please turn to page 224
Turn to the answer section on page 232 to find out if you've won ₹6,40,000

51

Which of the following is not a gymnastics event at the Olympics?

A: Parallel Bars
B: Madison
C: Trampoline
D: Horizontal Bars

52

Which sage took Rama and Lakshmana to Sita's swayamvara?

A: Valmiki
B: Gautama
C: Vashishtha
D: Vishwamitra

53

In which wildlife reserve was India's Project Tiger introduced in 1973?

A: Sundarbans
B: Jim Corbett
C: Kanha National Park
D: Ranthambhore

54

Which of these was a main character in Vishakhadatta's play 'Mudrarakshasa'?

A: Vishwamitra
B: Dushyanta
C: Ravana
D: Chanakya

55

What does the Big Bang theory deal with?

A: Atom Bomb
B: Origin of the Universe
C: Stock Market Crash
D: Nuclear Reactors

If you would like to use your 50:50 please turn to page 212
If you would like to Ask The Audience please turn to page 224
Turn to the answer section on page 232 to find out if you've won ₹6,40,000

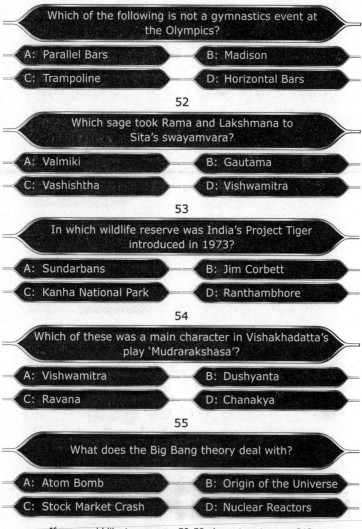

56

On which day of the year do Christians observe the 'twelfth night'?

A: 5th January

B: 25th December

C: 31st December

D: 23rd June

57

Which creature uses a phenomenon called echolocation to avoid obstacles?

A: Vulture

B: Bat

C: Eagle

D: Owl

58

Which politician was the President of the BCCI from 1990 to 1993?

A: N K P Salve

B: Sharad Pawar

C: Madhavrao Scindia

D: Suresh Kalmadi

59

Who was the British Governor-General during the 1857 War of Independence?

A: Lord Dalhousie

B: Lord Canning

C: Lord Elgin I

D: Lord Ripon

60

In which language did Kamban write his version of the Ramayana?

A: Sanskrit

B: Tamil

C: Malayalam

D: Telugu

If you would like to use your 50:50 please turn to page 212
If you would like to Ask The Audience please turn to page 224
Turn to the answer section on page 232 to find out if you've won ₹6,40,000

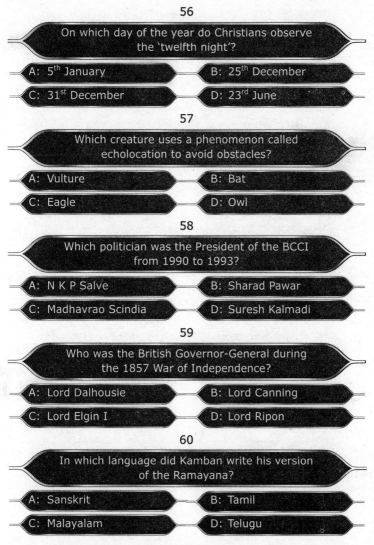

61

What is the Japanese business philosophy of continuous improvement called?

A: Karaoke
B: Kaizen
C: Kamikaze
D: Kimono

62

In which game is each session of play called a 'chukker'?

A: Kabbadi
B: Kho Kho
C: Polo
D: Gilli Danda

63

In Hindu tradition, which God is known as Ramakant?

A: Ganesha
B: Shiva
C: Brahma
D: Vishnu

64

Which army rank is the equivalent of an Air Commodore in the Air Force?

A: Major General
B: Colonel
C: Brigadier
D: Commander

65

Which of these is the most common species of deer found in India?

A: Indian Muntjac
B: Sambar
C: Barasingha
D: Sangai

If you would like to use your 50:50 please turn to page 212
If you would like to Ask The Audience please turn to page 224
Turn to the answer section on page 232 to find out if you've won ₹6,40,000

66

Which of the following would be normally found on the back cover of a book?

A: ISDN

B: ISBN

C: IRBM

D: ICBM

67

Who among these has not played the lead role in a film titled 'Ziddi'?

A: Joy Mukherjee

B: Sunny Deol

C: Dev Anand

D: Dilip Kumar

68

Which deity is primarily worshipped on Makar Sankranti?

A: Prithvi

B: Chandra

C: Surya

D: Laxmi

69

Who was the first ruling British monarch to visit India?

A: George V

B: Elizabeth II

C: Edward VIII

D: Victoria

70

With which company would you associate the Munjal brothers?

A: TTK Prestige

B: Titan Industries

C: Patni Computers

D: Hero Cycles

If you would like to use your 50:50 please turn to page 212
If you would like to Ask The Audience please turn to page 224
Turn to the answer section on page 232 to find out if you've won ₹6,40,000

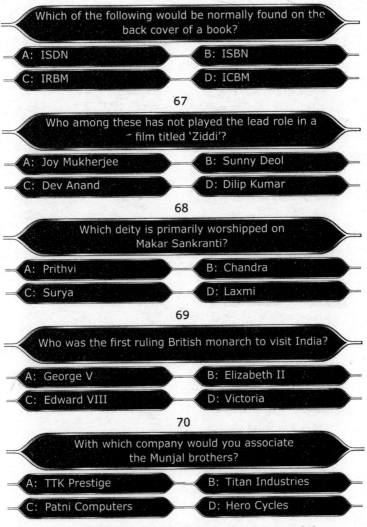

71

In whose cabinet was Indira Gandhi the Union Minister for Information and Broadcasting?

A: Morarji Desai
B: Lal Bahadur Shastri
C: Jawaharlal Nehru
D: Sardar Patel

72

In which city would you find the Calico Museum of Textiles?

A: Ahmedabad
B: Surat
C: Kozhikode
D: Panipat

73

'Tamra' is the Sanskrit word for which metal?

A: Gold
B: Silver
C: Copper
D: Bronze

74

Which is the only Olympic sport with a maximum weight limit?

A: Wrestling
B: Judo
C: Weight Lifting
D: Taekwondo

75

Which Soviet leader is associated with the terms 'Glasnost' and 'Perestroika'?

A: Mikhail Gorbachev
B: Boris Yeltsin
C: Vladimir Putin
D: Yuri Andropov

If you would like to use your 50:50 please turn to page 212
If you would like to Ask The Audience please turn to page 224
Turn to the answer section on page 232 to find out if you've won ₹6,40,000

76

In Hindu mythology, which Vedic sage's wife was Arundhati?

A: Vashishtha
B: Valmiki
C: Gautama
D: Agastya

77

The Tulu language is native to which state of India?

A: Andhra Pradesh
B: Orissa
C: Karnataka
D: Gujarat

78

To whom was Noorjahan married, before she married Emperor Jahangir?

A: Sheikh Multan
B: Sheikh Sultan
C: Sher Afghan
D: Sher Khan

79

What is the height of the hoop from ground in a standard basketball court?

A: 8 feet
B: 10 feet
C: 12 feet
D: 11 feet

80

Which of these films was based on a novel written in English?

A: Umrao Jaan
B: Lagaan
C: Junoon
D: Salaam Bombay

If you would like to use your 50:50 please turn to page 212
If you would like to Ask The Audience please turn to page 224
Turn to the answer section on page 232 to find out if you've won ₹6,40,000

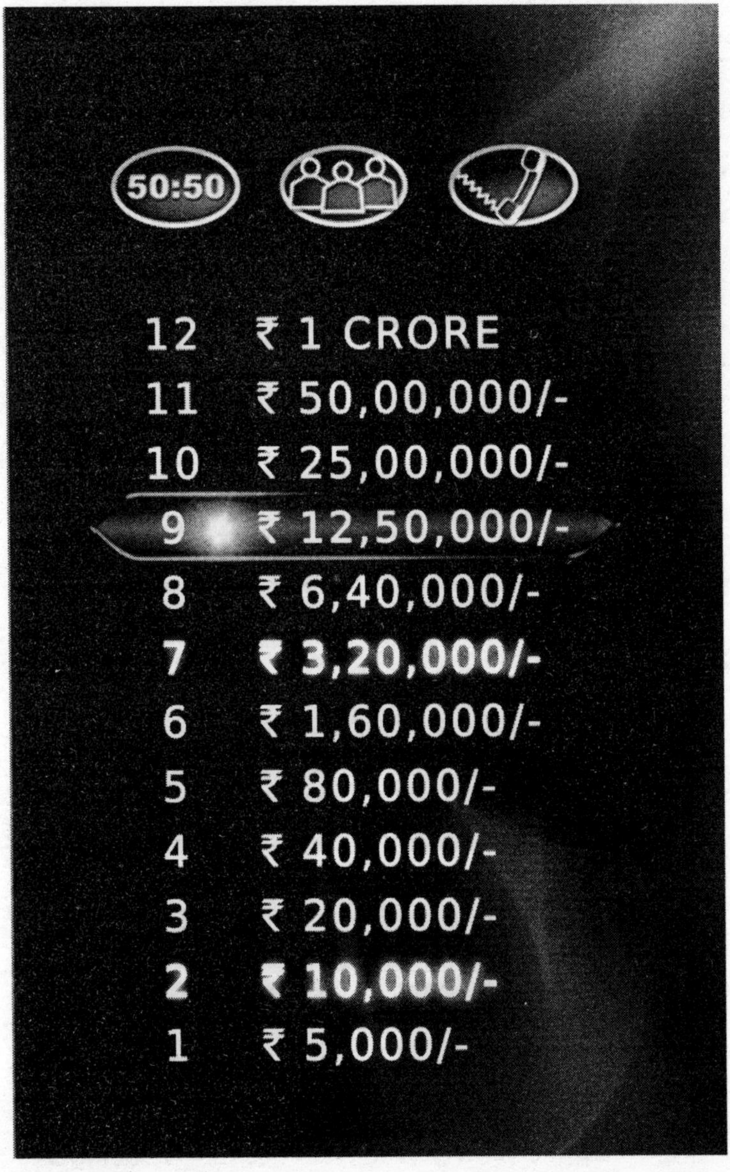

50:50
12 ₹ 1 CRORE
11 ₹ 50,00,000/-
10 ₹ 25,00,000/-
9 ₹ 12,50,000/-
8 ₹ 6,40,000/-
7 ₹ 3,20,000/-
6 ₹ 1,60,000/-
5 ₹ 80,000/-
4 ₹ 40,000/-
3 ₹ 20,000/-
2 ₹ 10,000/-
1 ₹ 5,000/-

9 ♦ ₹12,50,000

1

Who is the only woman to have received two Nobel Prizes?

A: Marie Curie
B: Aung San Su Kyi
C: Mother Teresa
D: Pearl S Buck

2

Who wrote the title song of the Hindi film 'Awara'?

A: Hasrat Jaipuri
B: Sahir Ludhianvi
C: Shailendra
D: Rahi Masoom Raza

3

Who was the first person to walk in space?

A: Alexei Leonov
B: John Glenn
C: Leonid Kizim
D: Yuri Romanenko

4

What name is given to a person who can recite the entire Koran from memory?

A: Mutawalli
B: Hafiz
C: Maulana
D: Khatib

5

Which court poet wrote the 'Akbarnama'?

A: Akbar
B: Abul Fazl
C: Birbal
D: Firdausi

If you would like to use your 50:50 please turn to page 212
If you would like to Ask The Audience please turn to page 224
Turn to the answer section on page 232 to find out if you've won ₹12,50,000

6

Which of these actors has not played nine different roles in one film?

A: Sivaji Ganesan

B: Sanjeev Kumar

C: Chiranjeevi

D: A Nageshwar Rao

7

To popularise which sport was the Silchar Club established in 1859?

A: Golf

B: Badminton

C: Polo

D: Football

8

Who wrote the 'Buddhacharita', a Sanskrit text based on the life of Buddha?

A: Ashvaghosha

B: Banabhatta

C: Bhavabhuti

D: Kalhana

9

Which Indian river is also known as Kalindi?

A: Yamuna

B: Sarayu

C: Ganga

D: Godavari

10

Which Mughal emperor's brothers were Kamran, Hindal and Askari?

A: Akbar

B: Shah Jahan

C: Humayun

D: Aurangzeb

If you would like to use your 50:50 please turn to page 212
If you would like to Ask The Audience please turn to page 224
Turn to the answer section on page 232 to find out if you've won ₹12,50,000

11

Which Indian umpire took more than 100 Test wickets as a bowler?

A: Rambabu Gupta
B: Swaroop Krishen
C: S Venkataraghavan
D: Piloo Reporter

12

To which gharana of Indian classical music did Bade Ghulam Ali Khan belong?

A: Kirana
B: Patiala
C: Gwalior
D: Agra

13

Which country gifted the Statue of Liberty to the United States of America?

A: Italy
B: France
C: UK
D: Ireland

14

In the Mahabharata, who created the 'chakravyuha'?

A: Dronacharya
B: Kripacharya
C: Jayadratha
D: Karna

15

What kind of weapon has been named the 'Pinaka' by the Indian Army ?

A: Tank
B: Rocket Launcher
C: Helicopter
D: Assault Rifle

If you would like to use your 50:50 please turn to page 212
If you would like to Ask The Audience please turn to page 224
Turn to the answer section on page 232 to find out if you've won ₹12,50,000

16

In which field did Sir Winston Churchill win a Nobel Prize in 1953?

A: Peace
B: Literature
C: Economics
D: Physics

17

Who has been the world's longest serving woman Prime Minister?

A: Golda Meir
B: Benazir Bhutto
C: Indira Gandhi
D: Margaret Thatcher

18

Who was the second man to set foot on the Moon?

A: Edwin Aldrin
B: John Glen
C: Alan Shepard
D: Chuck Yeager

19

Which legendary singer and actor was originally a typewriter salesman?

A: K L Saigal
B: Mukesh
C: Kishore Kumar
D: Talat Mehmood

20

What name was Tulsidas given at birth?

A: Atmaram
B: Rambola
C: Tulsiram
D: Purandhar Das

If you would like to use your 50:50 please turn to page 212
If you would like to Ask The Audience please turn to page 224
Turn to the answer section on page 232 to find out if you've won ₹12,50,000

21

Who was the Viceroy of India when the Quit India Movement was launched?

A: Lord Mountbatten
B: Lord Wavell
C: Lord Linlithgow
D: Lord Willingdon

22

Who is the only actor to play Akbar, Alexander and Porus in various Hindi films?

A: Sivaji Ganesan
B: K L Saigal
C: Prithviraj Kapoor
D: Mahipal

23

Which of these old princely states is now in Pakistan?

A: Junagarh
B: Malerkotla
C: Bahawalpur
D: Arcot

24

Which is India's first nuclear reactor?

A: Apsara
B: Menaka
C: Rambha
D: Urvashi

25

In which emperor's court did Varahamihira and Dhanwantari serve?

A: Samudragupta
B: Chandragupta II
C: Harshavardhana
D: Pulakesin II

If you would like to use your 50:50 please turn to page 212
If you would like to Ask The Audience please turn to page 224
Turn to the answer section on page 232 to find out if you've won ₹12,50,000

26

Where in India is the world's only floating wildlife sanctuary located?

A: Manipur
B: Meghalaya
C: Tripura
D: Assam

27

Which of these Prime Ministers was not born at Allahabad?

A: Indira Gandhi
B: V P Singh
C: Lal Bahadur Shastri
D: Jawaharlal Nehru

28

With which of the following would you associate Dr Verghese Kurien?

A: Operation Vijay
B: Project Tiger
C: Operation Flood
D: Operation Shakti

29

Which ruler of Delhi was originally called Farid Khan?

A: Aurangzeb
B: Sher Shah Suri
C: Humayun
D: Shah Jahan

30

Before Chandigarh, what was the capital of Punjab between 1947 and 1953?

A: Ambala
B: Amritsar
C: Simla
D: Patiala

If you would like to use your 50:50 please turn to page 212
If you would like to Ask The Audience please turn to page 224
Turn to the answer section on page 232 to find out if you've won ₹12,50,000

31

Which of Akbar's 'navratnas' was allegedly killed on Jahangir's order?

A: Tansen
B: Abul Fazl
C: Birbal
D: Faizi

32

Which bowler first claimed a hattrick in One Day International cricket?

A: Jalaluddin
B: Chetan Sharma
C: Richard Hadlee
D: Dennis Lillee

33

During which of these President's tenure did India see four Prime Ministers?

A: A P J Abdul Kalam
B: R Venkataraman
C: K R Narayanan
D: Zail Singh

34

Who is the masculine half of the deity Ardhanareeshwara?

A: Shiva
B: Indra
C: Yama
D: Brahma

35

How do we better know the Urdu poet Akhtar Hussain Rizvi?

A: Sahir Ludhianvi
B: Kaifi Azmi
C: Faiz Ahmed Faiz
D: Javed Akhtar

If you would like to use your 50:50 please turn to page 212
If you would like to Ask The Audience please turn to page 224
Turn to the answer section on page 232 to find out if you've won ₹12,50,000

36

Along with Agni, to which God are the most number of hymns in the Rig Veda dedicated?

A: Varuna
B: Vayu
C: Mitra
D: Indra

37

Which was the first Asian City to host the Commonwealth Games?

A: Singapore
B: Djakarta
C: Kuala Lumpur
D: Manila

38

Which Indian state has the longest coastline?

A: Kerala
B: Maharastra
C: Gujarat
D: Tamil Nadu

39

Which Governor-General of British India became the first Viceroy of India?

A: Lord Dalhousie
B: Lord Wellesley
C: Lord Canning
D: Lord Hastings

40

Which Chief Justice of India later served as the Vice President of India?

A: G S Pathak
B: B D Jatti
C: M Hidayatullah
D: Y V Chandrachud

If you would like to use your 50:50 please turn to page 212
If you would like to Ask The Audience please turn to page 224
Turn to the answer section on page 232 to find out if you've won ₹12,50,000

41

Who was the last Hindu king to rule Delhi?

A: Hemu

B: Rana Sanga

C: Shivaji

D: Rana Pratap

42

In Hindu tradition, which of these is one of the eight forms of marriage?

A: Kalyana

B: Magha

C: Gandharva

D: Saranga

43

The medical term hysterectomy refers to the removal of which organ?

A: Kidney

B: Liver

C: Lungs

D: Uterus

44

Which musical instrument is played using a wooden stick called danka?

A: Dumroo

B: Mridangam

C: Nagara

D: Bongo

45

In which category did Bhanu Athaiya share an Oscar for the film 'Gandhi'?

A: Best Actress

B: Best Director

C: Best Costume Design

D: Best Screenplay

If you would like to use your 50:50 please turn to page 213
If you would like to Ask The Audience please turn to page 225
Turn to the answer section on page 232 to find out if you've won ₹12,50,000

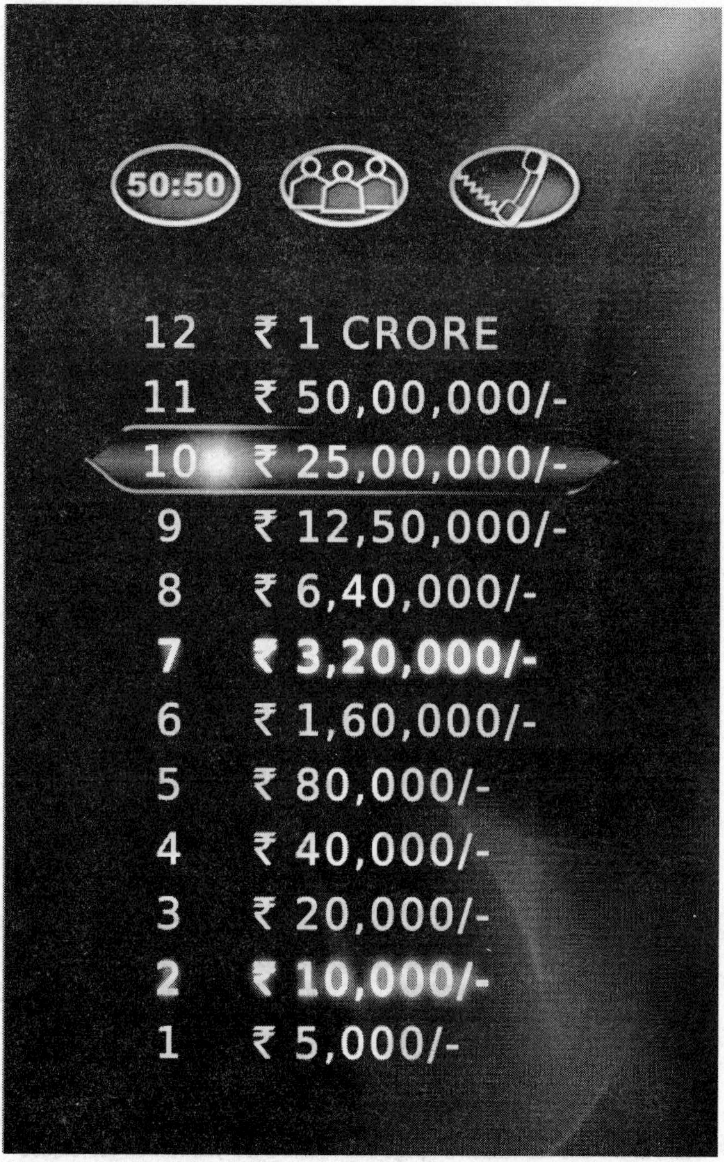
50:50
12 ₹ 1 CRORE
11 ₹ 50,00,000/-
10 ₹ 25,00,000/-
9 ₹ 12,50,000/-
8 ₹ 6,40,000/-
7 ₹ 3,20,000/-
6 ₹ 1,60,000/-
5 ₹ 80,000/-
4 ₹ 40,000/-
3 ₹ 20,000/-
2 ₹ 10,000/-
1 ₹ 5,000/-

10 ◆ ₹25,00,000

1

Which of these is a train run by the Indian Railways?

A: Royal Palace
B: Royal Queen
C: Royal Orient
D: Royal Safari

2

Who is the only Indian to score a hattrick in Olympic football?

A: Neville D'Souza
B: P K Banerjee
C: Shabbir Ali
D: Baichung Bhutia

3

Who wrote 'Rajmohan's Wife', the first novel in English by an Indian?

A: Sarat Chandra
B: Toru Dutt
C: Bankim Chandra
D: Sarojini Naidu

4

From which plant is the anti-malarial drug quinine obtained?

A: Wattle
B: Cinchona
C: Eucalyptus
D: Cinnamon

5

Which Rishi swallowed Ganga, later releasing her through his ears?

A: Agastya
B: Vashishtha
C: Bhagirathi
D: Jahnu

If you would like to use your 50:50 please turn to page 213
If you would like to Ask The Audience please turn to page 225
Turn to the answer section on page 233 to find out if you've won ₹25,00,000

6

Where was India's first planetarium built?

A: Delhi
B: Jaipur
C: Calcutta
D: Madras

7

Which is the largest state in the United States?

A: Alaska
B: Alabama
C: North Dakota
D: Texas

8

Which was the only Congress session presided over by Mahatma Gandhi?

A: Calcutta
B: Gaya
C: Belgaum
D: Bombay

9

How many characters made up of combinations of dots are used in Braille?

A: 49
B: 63
C: 75
D: 87

10

Which of these England Test captains was not born in India?

A: Nasser Hussain
B: Colin Cowdrey
C: Douglas Jardine
D: Ted Dexter

If you would like to use your 50:50 please turn to page 213
If you would like to Ask The Audience please turn to page 225
Turn to the answer section on page 233 to find out if you've won ₹25,00,000

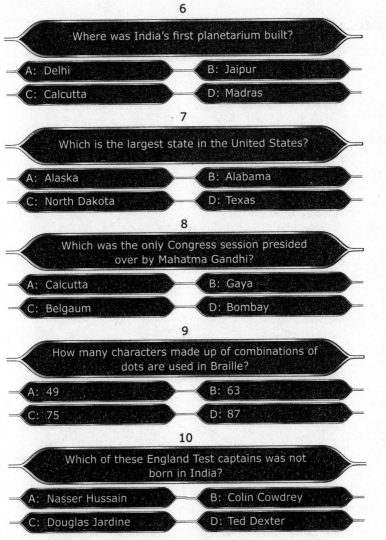

11

What is the 'vahana' of Goddess Ganga?

A: Naag
B: Simha
C: Hans
D: Makara

12

Who was the first film personality to be honoured with the Bharat Ratna?

A: Satyajit Ray
B: Lata Mangeshkar
C: M S Subbulaxmi
D: M G Ramachandran

13

What did John Logie Baird invent?

A: Microwave Oven
B: Television
C: Fax Machine
D: Photocopier

14

From which language has the word 'Punjab' been derived?

A: Greek
B: Arabic
C: Persian
D: Sanskrit

15

Which human organ did Christiaan Barnard first successfully transplant?

A: Liver
B: Brain
C: Kidney
D: Heart

If you would like to use your 50:50 please turn to page 213
If you would like to Ask The Audience please turn to page 225
Turn to the answer section on page 233 to find out if you've won ₹25,00,000

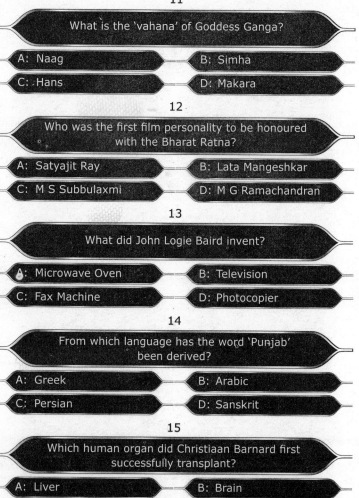

16

Which district of Puducherry lies within Andhra Pradesh?

A: Mahe
B: Yanam
C: Karaikal
D: Puducherry

17

Where did the Ahoms establish their capital in the 13th century?

A: Sibsagar
B: Pragjyotishpur
C: Tezpur
D: Dibrugarh

18

Who has been the youngest appointed governor of an Indian state?

A: Romesh Bhandari
B: Swaraj Kaushal
C: Motilal Vora
D: Bhai Mahavir

19

Which was India's first celluloid feature film made for television?

A: Sadgati
B: Janam
C: Shriman-Shrimati
D: Daddy

20

Which musical instrument was known as 'Shata Tantri Veena' in Sanskrit?

A: Sarod
B: Sitar
C: Rudra Veena
D: Santoor

If you would like to use your 50:50 please turn to page 213
If you would like to Ask The Audience please turn to page 225
Turn to the answer section on page 233 to find out if you've won ₹25,00,000

21

Where is the oldest Jewish synagogue in India?

A: Surat

B: Mumbai

C: Kochi

D: Kolkata

22

Who is the first Indian to win the All England badminton championship?

A: Saina Nehwal

B: Rajiv Bagga

C: Prakash Padukone

D: Vimal Kumar

23

In Hindu tradition, which of these is another name of Indra?

A: Mukunda

B: Madhava

C: Keshava

D: Purandara

24

In which state was the Bhoodan Movement launched by Vinoba Bhave?

A: Uttar Pradesh

B: Madhya Pradesh

C: Andhra Pradesh

D: Maharashtra

25

Which musician's autobiography is titled 'Raga Mala' ?

A: Kishori Amonkar

B: Amjad Ali Khan

C: Ravi Shankar

D: M S Subbulakshmi

If you would like to use your 50:50 please turn to page 213
If you would like to Ask The Audience please turn to page 225
Turn to the answer section on page 233 to find out if you've won ₹25,00,000

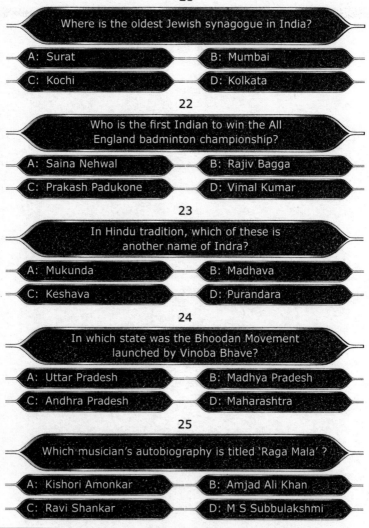

26

In which fort near Junnar was Chattrapati Shivaji born?

A: Raigadh
B: Shivneri
C: Janjira
D: Pratapgadh

27

Which of these is also the name of a place in Gujarat?

A: Sourav
B: Sachin
C: Rahul
D: Sunil

28

Where did Kasturba Gandhi die in detention?

A: Yeravada Jail
B: Sabarmati Ashram
C: Birla House
D: Aga Khan Palace

29

Which of these sports has never featured at the Olympics?

A: Cricket
B: Tug of War
C: Polo
D: Bowls

30

Which country rules the Falkland Islands in the Atlantic Ocean?

A: Argentina
B: UK
C: Germany
D: France

If you would like to use your 50:50 please turn to page 213
If you would like to Ask The Audience please turn to page 225
Turn to the answer section on page 233 to find out if you've won ₹25,00,000

31

Which Indian President has also been the Speaker of the Lok Sabha?

A: Zail Singh

B: N Sanjiva Reddy

C: S Radhakrishnan

D: R Venkataraman

32

Bhaskara II's work 'Lilavati' is a treatise on which subject?

A: Mathematics

B: Law

C: Astronomy

D: Astrology

33

Which of these cricketers acted in the 1973 Hindi film 'Charitra'?

A: Sunil Gavaskar

B: Salim Durrani

C: Sandeep Patil

D: Syed Abid Ali

34

In which jail did Pandit Nehru write the book 'The Discovery of India'?

A: Port Blair

B: Mandalay

C: Naini

D: Ahmednagar

35

Which former cricketer died of a heart attack while playing polo?

A: Ranjitsinhji

B: I A Khan Pataudi

C: Yadavindra Singh, Patiala

D: Duleepsinhji

If you would like to use your 50:50 please turn to page 213
If you would like to Ask The Audience please turn to page 225
Turn to the answer section on page 233 to find out if you've won ₹25,00,000

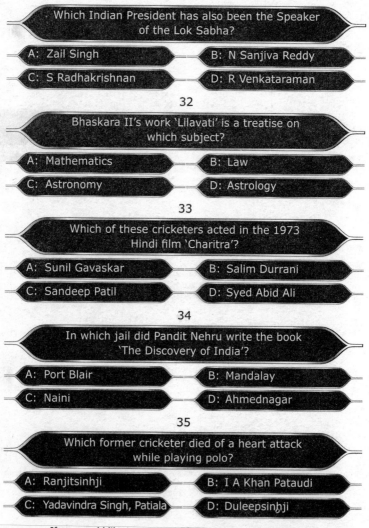

36

Who started his playback career in the 1944 Punjabi film 'Gul Baloch'?

A: K L Saigal
B: Talat Mahmood
C: Mohammad Rafi
D: Mahendra Kapoor

37

Ustad Isa is credited with being the architect of which monument?

A: Taj Mahal
B: Red Fort
C: Jama Masjid
D: Fatehpur Sikri

38

Who started the first Persian weekly journal in India, 'Mirat-ul-Akhbar'?

A: Vidyasagar
B: Ram Mohan Roy
C: Syed Ahmed Khan
D: Maulana Azad

39

Which of these fish migrates from the sea upriver to breed?

A: Rohu
B: Bombay Duck
C: Hilsa
D: Catla

40

What was the capital of the Vindhya Pradesh state between 1948 and 1956?

A: Raipur
B: Rewa
C: Raisen
D: Rajnandgaon

If you would like to use your 50:50 please turn to page 213
If you would like to Ask The Audience please turn to page 225
Turn to the answer section on page 233 to find out if you've won ₹25,00,000

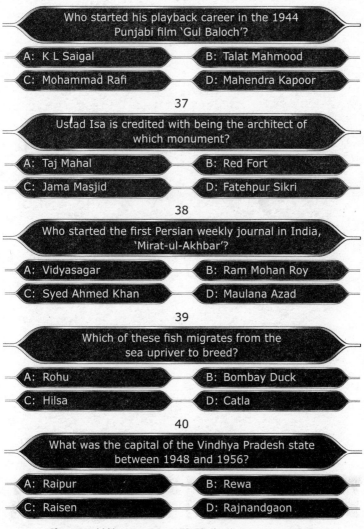

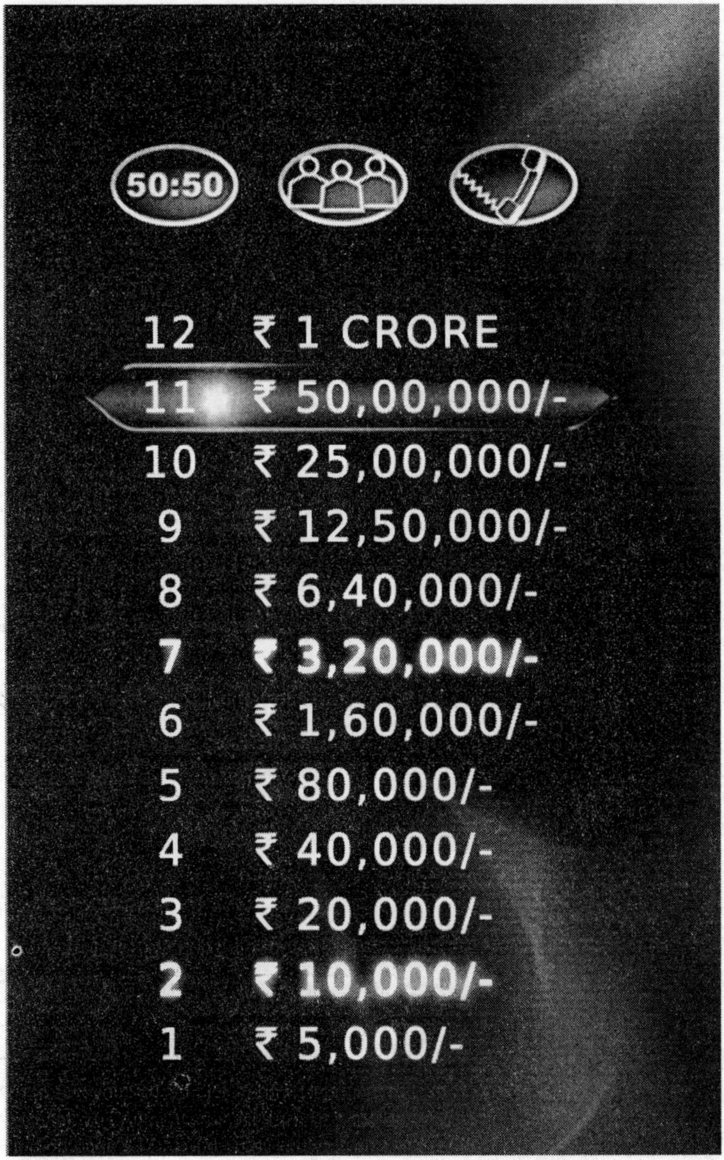
50:50
12 ₹ 1 CRORE
11 ₹ 50,00,000/-
10 ₹ 25,00,000/-
9 ₹ 12,50,000/-
8 ₹ 6,40,000/-
7 ₹ 3,20,000/-
6 ₹ 1,60,000/-
5 ₹ 80,000/-
4 ₹ 40,000/-
3 ₹ 20,000/-
2 ₹ 10,000/-
1 ₹ 5,000/-

1

Who invented the oral polio vaccine (OPV)?

A: Ronald Ross
B: Louis Pasteur
C: Francis Crick
D: Albert Sabin

2

Who founded the Bombay Talkies studio in 1934?

A: V Shantaram
B: Dadasaheb Phalke
C: Himanshu Rai
D: Ashok Kumar

3

Which was the first country to make Christianity the official religion?

A: Italy
B: England
C: Greece
D: Armenia

4

Who was the first Chief Justice of the Supreme Court of India?

A: Mehr Chand Khanna
B: K John Mathew
C: H J Kania
D: K N Wanchoo

5

Which of these cricketers played Test cricket for both India and Pakistan?

A: Dilawar Hussain
B: Amir Elahi
C: Jahangir Khan
D: Nasim-ul-Ghani

If you would like to use your 50:50 please turn to page 213
If you would like to Ask The Audience please turn to page 225
Turn to the answer section on page 233 to find out if you've won ₹50,00,000

6

Who was the first unopposed candidate to be elected VP of India?

A: Zakir Hussain
B: B D Jatti
C: V V Giri
D: S Radhakrishnan

7

Which two places were connected by India's first electric train?

A: Bombay - Thane
B: Howrah - Hooghly
C: Delhi - Agra
D: Bombay VT - Kurla

8

Which Indian monk founded the Madhyamaka or Middle Path school of Buddhism?

A: Mahendra
B: Nagarjuna
C: Nagasena
D: Kumarajiva

9

Which was the first Hindi film to use playback singing?

A: Dhoop Chhaon
B: Alam Ara
C: Noor Jahan
D: Bees Saal Baad

10

Where was the world's first fingerprinting bureau established?

A: Simla
B: Paris
C: New York
D: Calcutta

If you would like to use your 50:50 please turn to page 213
If you would like to Ask The Audience please turn to page 225
Turn to the answer section on page 233 to find out if you've won ₹50,00,000

11

Who wrote the script of the 1958 Bimal Roy classic film 'Madhumati'?

A: K A Abbas
B: Gulzar
C: Ritwik Ghatak
D: Javed Akhtar

12

Which Bharat Ratna recipient once served in the French Army?

A: Khan Abdul Ghaffar Khan
B: J R D Tata
C: Nelson Mandela
D: Pandurang Kane

13

Which of these was the precursor of the Devanagari script?

A: Sharada
B: Newari
C: Pali
D: Siddhamatrika

14

Which baby is officially considered to be India's one billionth child?

A: Asha
B: Astha
C: Akanksha
D: Anoushka

15

In Indian history, by what name is Fateh Ali Khan better known?

A: Hyder Ali
B: Muhammad Ghori
C: Mahmud of Ghazni
D: Tipu Sultan

If you would like to use your 50:50 please turn to page 213
If you would like to Ask The Audience please turn to page 225
Turn to the answer section on page 233 to find out if you've won ₹50,00,000

16

Which author's biography is titled 'Kalam Ka Sipahi'?

A: Amritlal Nagar
B: Acharya Shukla
C: Munshi Premchand
D: Bhishm Sahni

17

Which of these international hockey players was elected to the Lok Sabha?

A: Dhyan Chand
B: Ajit Pal Singh
C: Leslie Claudius
D: Aslam Sher Khan

18

Who first edited and translated the Rig Veda into English?

A: Max Muller
B: William Jones
C: Monear Williams
D: Maxim Gorky

19

Which scientist shared the Nobel Prize for Physics with the Curies in 1903?

A: Antoine Becquerel
B: Max Planck
C: Ernest Rutherford
D: Niels Bohr

20

Which of these MiG aircraft has never been used by the Indian Air Force?

A: MiG 21
B: MiG 19
C: MiG 25
D: MiG 29

If you would like to use your 50:50 please turn to page 213
If you would like to Ask The Audience please turn to page 225
Turn to the answer section on page 233 to find out if you've won ₹50,00,000

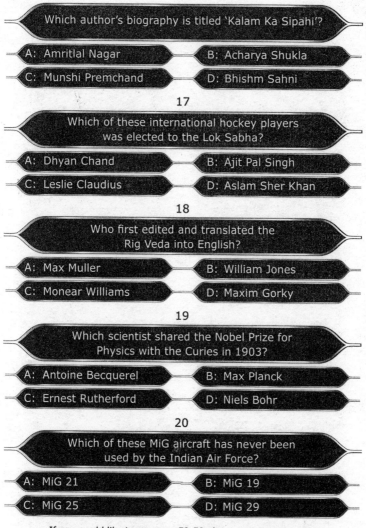

21

Which was the first Open University established in India in 1982?

A: Indira Gandhi
B: Nalanda
C: B R Ambedkar
D: Jawaharlal Nehru

22

In which American city was the Ghadar Party founded in 1913?

A: San Francisco
B: Los Angeles
C: Chicago
D: New York

23

A collection of poems by which actor was published as the 'Tanha Chand'?

A: Nargis
B: Waheeda Rehman
C: Meena Kumari
D: Deepti Naval

24

In the Mahabharata, whom did Karna kill using Indra's weapon 'Shakti'?

A: Drupad
B: Ghatotkacha
C: Abhimanyu
D: Satyaki

25

In 1965, who became the first recipient of the Jnanpith award?

A: Mahasweta Devi
B: Firaq Gorakhpuri
C: G Shankara Kurup
D: Jaishankar Prasad

If you would like to use your 50:50 please turn to page 213
If you would like to Ask The Audience please turn to page 225
Turn to the answer section on page 233 to find out if you've won ₹50,00,000

26

Which of these persons was never appointed Acting President of India?

A: V V Giri
B: Fakhruddin Ali Ahmed
C: M Hidayatullah
D: B D Jatti

27

Who was the first recipient of the Param Vir Chakra?

A: Shaitan Singh
B: Albert Ekka
C: Somnath Sharma
D: Hoshiar Singh

28

Off which bowler did Ravi Shastri score six sixes in one over in a first class match?

A: Arshad Ayub
B: Tilak Raj
C: Rajinder Goel
D: Tushar Arothe

29

Who was the Prime Minister of England when India became independent?

A: Clement Atlee
B: Winston Churchill
C: Anthony Eden
D: Harold Wilson

30

Which of these is not an official language of the United Nations?

A: Spanish
B: French
C: Italian
D: English

If you would like to use your 50:50 please turn to page 213
If you would like to Ask The Audience please turn to page 225
Turn to the answer section on page 233 to find out if you've won ₹50,00,000

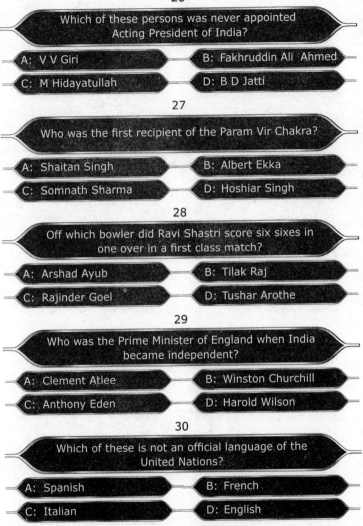

31

To investigate which event did Lord Chelmsford appoint the Hunter Committee in October 1919?

A: Chauri Chaura incident
B: Komagata Maru incident
C: Moplah rebellion
D: Jallianwalla Bagh massacre

32

Which Union Finance Minister introduced VDIS, or the Voluntary Disclosure of Income Scheme?

A: Yashwant Sinha
B: P Chidambaram
C: Manmohan Singh
D: Pranab Mukherjee

33

Who played the title role in the 1945 film 'Meera'?

A: Kanan Devi
B: M S Subbulakshmi
C: Sulochana
D: Devika Rani

34

Arati Pradhan became the first woman in the world to swim across which water body in 1988?

A: Strait of Gibraltar
B: English Channel
C: Palk Strait
D: Bosphorus

35

Which of these is the oldest Indian paramilitary force?

A: Assam Rifles
B: Border Security Force
C: Indo-Tibetan Border Police
D: National Security Guard

If you would like to use your 50:50 please turn to page 214
If you would like to Ask The Audience please turn to page 226
Turn to the answer section on page 233 to find out if you've won ₹50,00,000

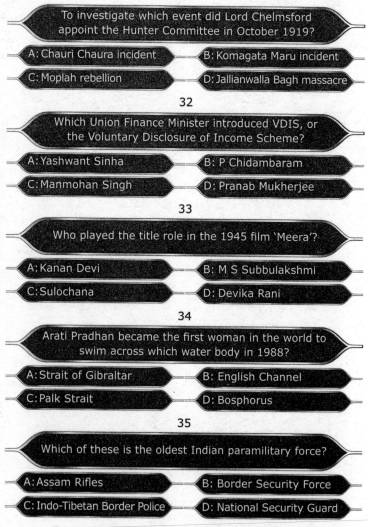

36

In Hindu mythology whose son was Bali?

A: Jambavan
B: Pavan
C: Indra
D: Shiva

37

Winston Churchill and Rudyard Kipling have both written for which Indian newspaper?

A: The Times of India
B: The Chronicle
C: The Pioneer
D: The Statesman

38

Which of these players has not won the Junior Wimbledon Singles title?

A: Ramesh Krishnan
B: Leander Paes
C: Ramanathan Krishnan
D: Vijay Amritraj

39

Who was Independent India's first Union Defence Minister?

A: Sardar Baldev Singh
B: Jagjivan Ram
C: Rafi Ahmed Kidwai
D: Rajkumari Amrit Kaur

40

Which poet was awarded the Jnanpith award in 1969 for his work 'Gul-e-Nagma'?

A: Sahir Ludhianvi
B: Jigar Muradabadi
C: Firakh Gorakhpuri
D: Asad Bhopali

If you would like to use your 50:50 please turn to page 214
If you would like to Ask The Audience please turn to page 226
Turn to the answer section on page 233 to find out if you've won ₹50,00,000

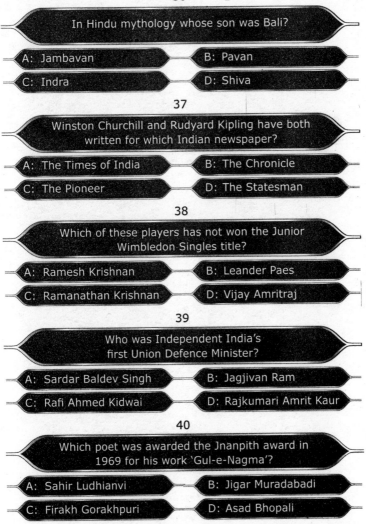

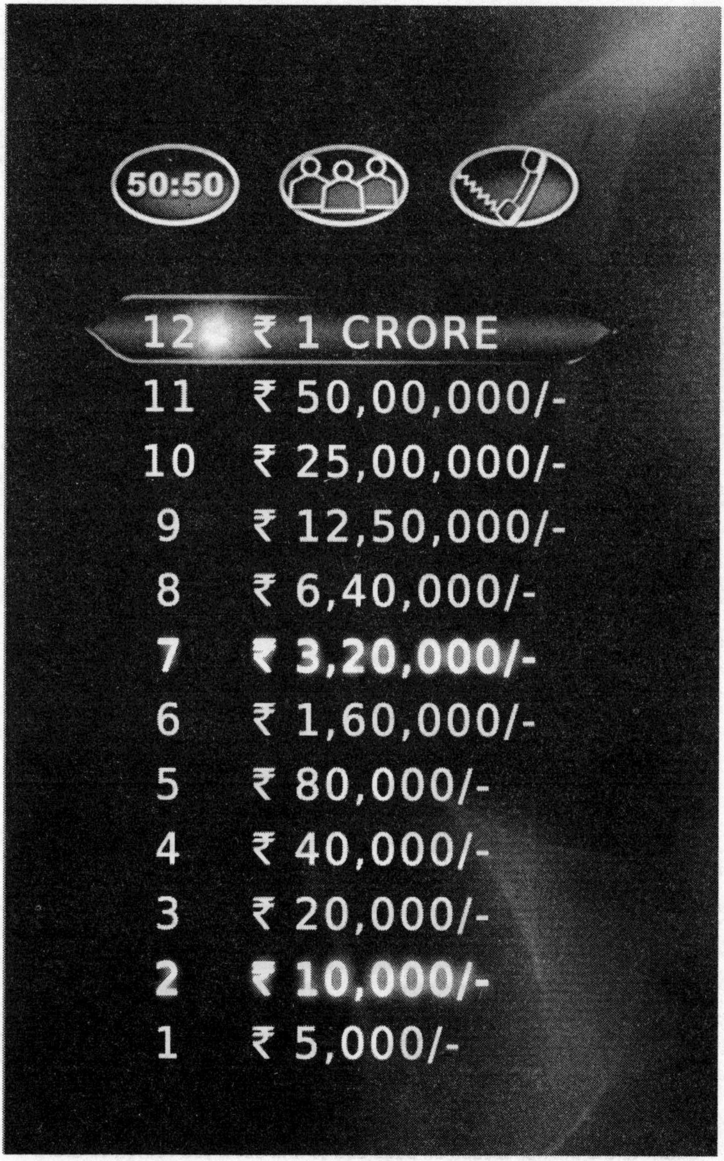
50:50
12 ₹ 1 CRORE
11 ₹ 50,00,000/-
10 ₹ 25,00,000/-
9 ₹ 12,50,000/-
8 ₹ 6,40,000/-
7 ₹ 3,20,000/-
6 ₹ 1,60,000/-
5 ₹ 80,000/-
4 ₹ 40,000/-
3 ₹ 20,000/-
2 ₹ 10,000/-
1 ₹ 5,000/-

12 ◆ ₹1 Crore

1

Which was the first National Park in India?

A: Jaisalmer Desert

B: Kanha

C: Gir

D: Hailey

2

Which of these awards was designed by Eva Savitribai Khanolkar?

A: Param Vir Chakra

B: Jnanpith Award

C: Bharat Ratna

D: Miss India crown

3

Who performed the first recorded hattrick in Ranji Trophy matches?

A: Baqa Jilani

B: A G Ram Singh

C: Mohammad Nissar

D: Ladha Amar Singh

4

Who among these was never the President of the Indian National Congress?

A: George Yule

B: Henry Cotton

C: Richard Bourke

D: Alfred Webb

5

Who was the first woman to be appointed Chief Justice of a High Court in India?

A: Noor Fatima Bibi

B: Leila Seth

C: Lata Patel

D: Anna Chandy

If you would like to use your 50:50 please turn to page 214
If you would like to Ask The Audience please turn to page 226
Turn to the answer section on page 233 to find out if you've won ₹1 Crore

6

What words were inscribed on the first postage stamp issued in independent India?

A: Vande Mataram
B: Satyamev Jayate
C: Jai Hind
D: Azad Hind

7

Who was independent India's first ambassador to the USSR?

A: Sarojini Naidu
B: S Radhakrishnan
C: Acharya Kripalani
D: Vijayalakshmi Pandit

8

Which sect was founded by the Agra banker Shiv Dayal Saheb in 1861?

A: Namdhari
B: Brahmakumari
C: Radha Soami Satsang
D: Deva Samaj

9

Which of these forts was not built by European colonial powers in India?

A: Fort Dansborg
B: Fort Naarden
C: Fort Chambray
D: Corjuem Fort

10

Which is the southernmost point of the continent of Africa?

A: Cape Agulhas
B: Cape Horn
C: Cape of Good Hope
D: Cape Hatteras

If you would like to use your 50:50 please turn to page 214
If you would like to Ask The Audience please turn to page 226
Turn to the answer section on page 233 to find out if you've won ₹1 Crore

11

By what name was Port Blair originally known?

A: Port Cornwallis
B: Port Wellesley
C: Port Dalhousie
D: Port Bentinck

12

Who was the first Secretary of State of the United States of America?

A: James Madison
B: John Quincy Adams
C: Thomas Jefferson
D: James Monroe

13

Who first held the rank of Air Chief Marshal in the Indian Air Force?

A: Arjan Singh
B: Thomas Elmhirst
C: Subroto Mukherjee
D: P C Lal

14

Who was the first Indian to be awarded the Victoria Cross?

A: Khudadad Khan
B: Agan Singh Rai
C: Netra Bahadur
D: Juma Mohammed

15

Which freedom fighter started the 'Bihar Law Weekly' in 1916?

A: Rajendra Prasad
B: Sachidanand Sinha
C: Dadasaheb Phalke
D: Ram Manohar Lohia

If you would like to use your 50:50 please turn to page 214
If you would like to Ask The Audience please turn to page 226
Turn to the answer section on page 233 to find out if you've won ₹1 Crore

16

Which actor captained England in his only appearance in Test cricket?

A: William Holden
B: C Aubrey Smith
C: Alan Ladd
D: W C Fields

17

Who became the first recipient of the Jnanpith Award for work in Sanskrit?

A: Gurdial Singh
B: Satyavrat Shastri
C: Bhai Veer Singh
D: Nirmal Verma

18

Which district of Assam became part of Pakistan after the 1947 plebiscite?

A: Tinsukia
B: Lohit
C: Nalbari
D: Sylhet

19

Who first climbed the highest peak on each of all the seven continents?

A: Daniel Johnson
B: Dick Bass
C: Phil Hartman
D: Reinhold Messner

20

Who was the first woman to produce a Hindi film, in which she also acted?

A: Fatima Begum
B: Kamla Bai
C: Nasreen
D: Zubeida

If you would like to use your 50:50 please turn to page 214
If you would like to Ask The Audience please turn to page 226
Turn to the answer section on page 233 to find out if you've won ₹1 Crore

21

Which branch of Ayurveda deals with mental disorders?

A: Kaayachikitsa
B: Bhutavidya
C: Vaajikarna
D: Rasaayana

22

Whose father was Aghorenath Chattopadhyay, Principal of Nizam's College?

A: Nellie Sengupta
B: Sucheta Kripalani
C: Sarojini Naidu
D: Aruna Asaf Ali

23

How many obstacles are there in the 3000 m steeplechase athletic event?

A: 16
B: 35
C: 24
D: 32

24

Who among the following was awarded the Param Vir Chakra posthumously?

A: Yogendra Yadav
B: Bana Singh
C: Abdul Hamid
D: Sanjay Kumar

25

Which Mughal Emperor's first ten years' rule does the 'Padshahnama' chronicle?

A: Akbar
B: Shah Jahan
C: Jahangir
D: Aurangzeb

If you would like to use your 50:50 please turn to page 214
If you would like to Ask The Audience please turn to page 226
Turn to the answer section on page 233 to find out if you've won ₹1 Crore

50:50

1 ◆ ₹5,000

1. options remaining are A and D
2. options remaining are C and B
3. options remaining are D and C
4. options remaining are D and C
5. options remaining are C and B
6. options remaining are B and A
7. options remaining are A and D
8. options remaining are A and B
9. options remaining are D and B
10. options remaining are C and D
11. options remaining are C and A
12. options remaining are C and B
13. options remaining are D and C
14. options remaining are A and D
15. options remaining are C and B
16. options remaining are C and D
17. options remaining are B and D
18. options remaining are D and A
19. options remaining are B and D
20. options remaining are B and D
21. options remaining are D and B
22. options remaining are C and D
23. options remaining are B and D
24. options remaining are B and A
25. options remaining are D and A
26. options remaining are B and D
27. options remaining are A and B
28. options remaining are B and A
29. options remaining are C and B
30. options remaining are A and B
31. options remaining are D and B
32. options remaining are D and C
33. options remaining are A and C
34. options remaining are C and B
35. options remaining are A and C
36. options remaining are C and B
37. options remaining are B and A
38. options remaining are B and A
39. options remaining are D and A
40. options remaining are C and D
41. options remaining are D and C
42. options remaining are D and C
43. options remaining are B and D
44. options remaining are C and B
45. options remaining are C and D
46. options remaining are C and A
47. options remaining are B and A
48. options remaining are A and C
49. options remaining are D and A
50. options remaining are D and B
51. options remaining are D and B
52. options remaining are C and B
53. options remaining are D and A
54. options remaining are C and D
55. options remaining are D and B
56. options remaining are B and A
57. options remaining are C and D
58. options remaining are D and C
59. options remaining are D and B
60. options remaining are B and C
61. options remaining are A and B
62. options remaining are B and C
63. options remaining are C and D
64. options remaining are D and B
65. options remaining are B and D
66. options remaining are C and A
67. options remaining are C and A
68. options remaining are D and A

69. options remaining are B and A
70. options remaining are C and A
71. options remaining are A and C
72. options remaining are B and D
73. options remaining are B and C
74. options remaining are C and B
75. options remaining are A and B
76. options remaining are D and A
77. options remaining are C and B
78. options remaining are C and A
79. options remaining are A and C
80. options remaining are C and D
81. options remaining are D and B
82. options remaining are C and B
83. options remaining are D and B
84. options remaining are C and A
85. options remaining are B and C
86. options remaining are C and A
87. options remaining are C and B
88. options remaining are D and C
89. options remaining are B and C
90. options remaining are B and C
91. options remaining are D and C
92. options remaining are A and D
93. options remaining are D and B
94. options remaining are B and A
95. options remaining are C and D
96. options remaining are B and C
97. options remaining are B and A
98. options remaining are D and A
99. options remaining are D and A
100. options remaining are C and A
101. options remaining are C and A
102. options remaining are B and A
103. options remaining are C and D
104. options remaining are D and C
105. options remaining are B and A
106. options remaining are C and A
107. options remaining are C and D
108. options remaining are B and A
109. options remaining are B and A
110. options remaining are C and D
111. options remaining are B and C
112. options remaining are C and B
113. options remaining are C and A
114. options remaining are C and B
115. options remaining are B and C
116. options remaining are D and B
117. options remaining are B and C
118. options remaining are C and A
119. options remaining are D and B
120. options remaining are B and A

2 ♦ ₹10,000

1. options remaining are B and C
2. options remaining are C and D
3. options remaining are B and A
4. options remaining are D and A
5. options remaining are B and C
6. options remaining are A and C
7. options remaining are B and D
8. options remaining are B and D
9. options remaining are C and A
10. options remaining are D and B
11. options remaining are C and D
12. options remaining are A and B
13. options remaining are B and C
14. options remaining are B and A
15. options remaining are C and A
16. options remaining are C and D
17. options remaining are D and A
18. options remaining are A and C
19. options remaining are B and A
20. options remaining are C and D
21. options remaining are B and A
22. options remaining are D and A
23. options remaining are B and D
24. options remaining are C and B
25. options remaining are C and D
26. options remaining are D and C
27. options remaining are A and D
28. options remaining are A and C

29. options remaining are D and A
30. options remaining are C and A
31. options remaining are A and B
32. options remaining are C and D
33. options remaining are C and B
34. options remaining are B and C
35. options remaining are C and A
36. options remaining are C and A
37. options remaining are B and D
38. options remaining are B and A
39. options remaining are C and D
40. options remaining are B and C
41. options remaining are C and A
42. options remaining are A and B
43. options remaining are A and B
44. options remaining are D and B
45. options remaining are B and C
46. options remaining are D and A
47. options remaining are B and C
48. options remaining are C and B
49. options remaining are A and B
50. options remaining are A and D
51. options remaining are D and C
52. options remaining are B and C
53. options remaining are A and C
54. options remaining are B and A
55. options remaining are C and B
56. options remaining are D and A
57. options remaining are C and D
58. options remaining are A and B
59. options remaining are C and B
60. options remaining are B and C
61. options remaining are D and C
62. options remaining are A and D
63. options remaining are D and A
64. options remaining are D and B
65. options remaining are A and C
66. options remaining are D and C
67. options remaining are A and B
68. options remaining are B and C
69. options remaining are C and A
70. options remaining are D and A
71. options remaining are B and A
72. options remaining are C and B
73. options remaining are A and B
74. options remaining are C and A
75. options remaining are D and A
76. options remaining are A and C
77. options remaining are A and C
78. options remaining are D and C
79. options remaining are C and A
80. options remaining are C and D
81. options remaining are D and C
82. options remaining are D and B
83. options remaining are C and D
84. options remaining are D and C
85. options remaining are C and A
86. options remaining are C and B
87. options remaining are B and A
88. options remaining are C and A
89. options remaining are A and C
90. options remaining are D and C
91. options remaining are C and A
92. options remaining are C and D
93. options remaining are D and A
94. options remaining are A and B
95. options remaining are C and A
96. options remaining are A and B
97. options remaining are D and B
98. options remaining are C and A
99. options remaining are B and A
100. options remaining are D and B
101. options remaining are D and C
102. options remaining are D and C
103. options remaining are C and D
104. options remaining are C and A
105. options remaining are D and C
106. options remaining are C and B
107. options remaining are B and D
108. options remaining are B and C
109. options remaining are D and A
110. options remaining are C and A
111. options remaining are A and C
112. options remaining are C and D
113. options remaining are C and D
114. options remaining are A and C

115. options remaining are D and B
116. options remaining are A and D
117. options remaining are D and B
118. options remaining are C and D
119. options remaining are C and D
120. options remaining are B and A

3 ♦ ₹20,000

1. options remaining are B and C
2. options remaining are D and C
3. options remaining are B and D
4. options remaining are C and A
5. options remaining are B and D
6. options remaining are C and A
7. options remaining are B and C
8. options remaining are C and B
9. options remaining are C and A
10. options remaining are B and A
11. options remaining are B and D
12. options remaining are A and C
13. options remaining are D and B
14. options remaining are C and B
15. options remaining are B and D
16. options remaining are B and C
17. options remaining are C and D
18. options remaining are D and A
19. options remaining are C and D
20. options remaining are A and D
21. options remaining are D and A
22. options remaining are B and C
23. options remaining are C and A
24. options remaining are B and A
25. options remaining are A and C
26. options remaining are D and A
27. options remaining are C and B
28. options remaining are D and A
29. options remaining are A and D
30. options remaining are B and A
31. options remaining are D and B
32. options remaining are B and A
33. options remaining are D and C
34. options remaining are D and C
35. options remaining are C and B
36. options remaining are A and B
37. options remaining are D and C
38. options remaining are C and A
39. options remaining are A and C
40. options remaining are C and D
41. options remaining are B and C
42. options remaining are A and B
43. options remaining are A and C
44. options remaining are C and B
45. options remaining are D and B
46. options remaining are A and D
47. options remaining are A and B
48. options remaining are D and C
49. options remaining are C and A
50. options remaining are C and B
51. options remaining are A and B
52. options remaining are B and D
53. options remaining are B and C
54. options remaining are D and C
55. options remaining are B and D
56. options remaining are C and D
57. options remaining are C and A
58. options remaining are A and D
59. options remaining are B and D
60. options remaining are D and B
61. options remaining are D and B
62. options remaining are C and B
63. options remaining are D and A
64. options remaining are C and A
65. options remaining are B and D
66. options remaining are B and D
67. options remaining are A and B
68. options remaining are D and B
69. options remaining are C and A
70. options remaining are B and C
71. options remaining are C and D
72. options remaining are C and A
73. options remaining are B and A
74. options remaining are C and B

75. options remaining are C and B
76. options remaining are D and B
77. options remaining are B and C
78. options remaining are B and A
79. options remaining are D and A
80. options remaining are B and C
81. options remaining are B and A
82. options remaining are C and A
83. options remaining are A and D
84. options remaining are B and D
85. options remaining are D and A
86. options remaining are C and A
87. options remaining are D and A
88. options remaining are C and D
89. options remaining are B and A
90. options remaining are C and A
91. options remaining are C and B
92. options remaining are D and B
93. options remaining are B and D
94. options remaining are A and D
95. options remaining are C and A
96. options remaining are D and C
97. options remaining are B and D
98. options remaining are A and B
99. options remaining are D and C
100. options remaining are A and C

4 ✦ ₹40,000

1. options remaining are C and A
2. options remaining are A and D
3. options remaining are B and C
4. options remaining are C and B
5. options remaining are B and A
6. options remaining are D and C
7. options remaining are C and B
8. options remaining are B and A
9. options remaining are A and C
10. options remaining are A and C
11. options remaining are A and D
12. options remaining are C and D
13. options remaining are C and B
14. options remaining are D and B
15. options remaining are D and A
16. options remaining are C and A
17. options remaining are C and D
18. options remaining are B and A
19. options remaining are A and C
20. options remaining are B and C
21. options remaining are C and D
22. options remaining are C and B
23. options remaining are A and B
24. options remaining are B and A
25. options remaining are C and A
26. options remaining are C and D
27. options remaining are B and A
28. options remaining are C and A
29. options remaining are B and C
30. options remaining are D and A
31. options remaining are D and C
32. options remaining are B and A
33. options remaining are B and C
34. options remaining are A and C
35. options remaining are C and B
36. options remaining are B and C
37. options remaining are C and B
38. options remaining are A and B
39. options remaining are A and B
40. options remaining are B and A
41. options remaining are B and C
42. options remaining are D and B
43. options remaining are C and B
44. options remaining are B and C
45. options remaining are A and D
46. options remaining are D and A
47. options remaining are D and C
48. options remaining are A and C
49. options remaining are D and B
50. options remaining are D and C
51. options remaining are B and D
52. options remaining are C and D
53. options remaining are B and C
54. options remaining are B and A

55. options remaining are C and B
56. options remaining are C and A
57. options remaining are B and D
58. options remaining are B and D
59. options remaining are C and A
60. options remaining are B and A
61. options remaining are B and A
62. options remaining are D and C
63. options remaining are C and A
64. options remaining are C and B
65. options remaining are A and C
66. options remaining are C and B
67. options remaining are C and A
68. options remaining are A and C
69. options remaining are B and C
70. options remaining are B and C
71. options remaining are A and D
72. options remaining are A and C
73. options remaining are B and D
74. options remaining are B and A
75. options remaining are D and A
76. options remaining are D and C
77. options remaining are A and D
78. options remaining are B and D
79. options remaining are D and B
80. options remaining are D and A
81. options remaining are A and B
82. options remaining are D and B
83. options remaining are B and A
84. options remaining are A and B
85. options remaining are C and A
86. options remaining are B and A
87. options remaining are C and B
88. options remaining are A and D
89. options remaining are B and C
90. options remaining are D and A

5 ✦ ₹80,000

1. options remaining are D and A
2. options remaining are B and C
3. options remaining are C and D
4. options remaining are A and B
5. options remaining are B and D
6. options remaining are A and B
7. options remaining are A and C
8. options remaining are D and B
9. options remaining are B and A
10. options remaining are B and C
11. options remaining are A and C
12. options remaining are A and D
13. options remaining are D and B
14. options remaining are B and D
15. options remaining are A and C
16. options remaining are D and B
17. options remaining are A and C
18. options remaining are B and A
19. options remaining are C and B
20. options remaining are C and A
21. options remaining are D and C
22. options remaining are B and A
23. options remaining are B and D
24. options remaining are A and C
25. options remaining are C and D
26. options remaining are D and A
27. options remaining are C and A
28. options remaining are A and B
29. options remaining are D and A
30. options remaining are B and C
31. options remaining are B and A
32. options remaining are B and A
33. options remaining are D and B
34. options remaining are C and D
35. options remaining are C and D
36. options remaining are B and C
37. options remaining are B and A
38. options remaining are D and B
39. options remaining are D and B
40. options remaining are A and B
41. options remaining are B and A
42. options remaining are C and D
43. options remaining are B and C
44. options remaining are D and A

45. options remaining are D and C
46. options remaining are B and D
47. options remaining are C and D
48. options remaining are A and C
49. options remaining are B and D
50. options remaining are C and D
51. options remaining are D and B
52. options remaining are A and B
53. options remaining are B and A
54. options remaining are A and B
55. options remaining are B and A
56. options remaining are B and A
57. options remaining are B and C
58. options remaining are D and C
59. options remaining are C and B
60. options remaining are B and A
61. options remaining are A and D
62. options remaining are A and D
63. options remaining are C and A
64. options remaining are B and A
65. options remaining are C and A
66. options remaining are C and B
67. options remaining are D and B
68. options remaining are B and A
69. options remaining are C and D
70. options remaining are A and B
71. options remaining are B and C
72. options remaining are B and A
73. options remaining are B and C
74. options remaining are D and C
75. options remaining are C and D
76. options remaining are D and C
77. options remaining are D and C
78. options remaining are B and C
79. options remaining are D and B
80. options remaining are C and D

6 ♦ ₹1,60,000

1. options remaining are B and C
2. options remaining are B and A
3. options remaining are C and A
4. options remaining are B and D
5. options remaining are B and A
6. options remaining are C and A
7. options remaining are D and C
8. options remaining are C and D
9. options remaining are A and D
10. options remaining are D and C
11. options remaining are C and D
12. options remaining are D and A
13. options remaining are C and D
14. options remaining are D and A
15. options remaining are B and C
16. options remaining are A and B
17. options remaining are C and A
18. options remaining are A and B
19. options remaining are D and B
20. options remaining are B and C
21. options remaining are C and A
22. options remaining are C and B
23. options remaining are A and B
24. options remaining are D and B
25. options remaining are A and D
26. options remaining are C and D
27. options remaining are C and D
28. options remaining are C and B
29. options remaining are D and C
30. options remaining are B and C
31. options remaining are C and A
32. options remaining are D and A
33. options remaining are B and D
34. options remaining are D and B
35. options remaining are B and C
36. options remaining are D and C
37. options remaining are B and D
38. options remaining are D and A
39. options remaining are B and A
40. options remaining are A and B
41. options remaining are A and C
42. options remaining are D and B
43. options remaining are D and A
44. options remaining are B and C

45. options remaining are C and D
46. options remaining are A and D
47. options remaining are A and B
48. options remaining are D and A
49. options remaining are C and B
50. options remaining are B and A
51. options remaining are C and A
52. options remaining are D and A
53. options remaining are C and A
54. options remaining are C and B
55. options remaining are B and C
56. options remaining are B and A
57. options remaining are A and D
58. options remaining are A and B
59. options remaining are D and B
60. options remaining are B and C
61. options remaining are D and A
62. options remaining are A and D
63. options remaining are C and B
64. options remaining are B and A
65. options remaining are B and C
66. options remaining are C and A
67. options remaining are C and A
68. options remaining are B and A
69. options remaining are A and D
70. options remaining are B and D
71. options remaining are D and C
72. options remaining are B and D
73. options remaining are B and D
74. options remaining are C and B
75. options remaining are D and C
76. options remaining are D and C
77. options remaining are B and C
78. options remaining are A and B
79. options remaining are B and D
80. options remaining are B and A

7 ◆ ₹3,20,000

1. options remaining are B and A
2. options remaining are D and C
3. options remaining are B and C
4. options remaining are C and B
5. options remaining are A and B
6. options remaining are B and C
7. options remaining are C and D
8. options remaining are B and A
9. options remaining are B and D
10. options remaining are D and A
11. options remaining are C and A
12. options remaining are C and D
13. options remaining are C and A
14. options remaining are D and A
15. options remaining are B and D
16. options remaining are D and A
17. options remaining are D and B
18. options remaining are D and A
19. options remaining are C and D
20. options remaining are B and A
21. options remaining are C and B
22. options remaining are B and A
23. options remaining are A and C
24. options remaining are B and C
25. options remaining are A and C
26. options remaining are C and B
27. options remaining are B and A
28. options remaining are D and A
29. options remaining are D and C
30. options remaining are A and C
31. options remaining are B and C
32. options remaining are A and B
33. options remaining are C and A
34. options remaining are B and D
35. options remaining are A and C
36. options remaining are B and A
37. options remaining are C and A
38. options remaining are C and D
39. options remaining are A and B
40. options remaining are A and B
41. options remaining are C and B
42. options remaining are A and C
43. options remaining are A and C
44. options remaining are B and A

45. options remaining are B and D
46. options remaining are C and D
47. options remaining are A and C
48. options remaining are C and B
49. options remaining are B and A
50. options remaining are C and B
51. options remaining are A and B
52. options remaining are B and C
53. options remaining are D and A
54. options remaining are C and B
55. options remaining are B and C
56. options remaining are D and C
57. options remaining are D and B
58. options remaining are C and B
59. options remaining are C and D
60. options remaining are A and C
61. options remaining are C and A
62. options remaining are C and B
63. options remaining are B and A
64. options remaining are A and B
65. options remaining are B and D
66. options remaining are C and D
67. options remaining are D and A
68. options remaining are A and D
69. options remaining are C and D
70. options remaining are B and A
71. options remaining are C and D
72. options remaining are B and A
73. options remaining are B and A
74. options remaining are C and D
75. options remaining are B and D
76. options remaining are B and D
77. options remaining are B and A
78. options remaining are A and C
79. options remaining are C and B
80. options remaining are D and A

8 ✦ ₹6,40,000

1. options remaining are C and B
2. options remaining are B and C
3. options remaining are C and B
4. options remaining are C and A
5. options remaining are D and A
6. options remaining are A and C
7. options remaining are C and D
8. options remaining are C and A
9. options remaining are B and C
10. options remaining are C and B
11. options remaining are C and A
12. options remaining are A and B
13. options remaining are D and B
14. options remaining are C and A
15. options remaining are B and D
16. options remaining are C and B
17. options remaining are B and D
18. options remaining are C and A
19. options remaining are B and A
20. options remaining are D and B
21. options remaining are B and D
22. options remaining are C and D
23. options remaining are A and D
24. options remaining are B and A
25. options remaining are D and C
26. options remaining are B and D
27. options remaining are B and A
28. options remaining are B and C
29. options remaining are D and B
30. options remaining are B and C
31. options remaining are C and D
32. options remaining are D and C
33. options remaining are A and B
34. options remaining are B and D
35. options remaining are C and D
36. options remaining are D and B
37. options remaining are C and B
38. options remaining are B and A
39. options remaining are B and D
40. options remaining are C and B
41. options remaining are C and B
42. options remaining are C and A

43. options remaining are B and C
44. options remaining are C and D
45. options remaining are C and B
46. options remaining are B and A
47. options remaining are C and A
48. options remaining are B and D
49. options remaining are D and C
50. options remaining are A and D
51. options remaining are B and C
52. options remaining are D and C
53. options remaining are B and A
54. options remaining are D and B
55. options remaining are B and D
56. options remaining are A and C
57. options remaining are B and C
58. options remaining are C and A
59. options remaining are B and A
60. options remaining are B and C
61. options remaining are B and C
62. options remaining are C and A
63. options remaining are D and A
64. options remaining are C and A
65. options remaining are B and C
66. options remaining are B and A
67. options remaining are D and C
68. options remaining are C and A
69. options remaining are A and D
70. options remaining are D and A
71. options remaining are B and C
72. options remaining are A and C
73. options remaining are C and D
74. options remaining are A and C
75. options remaining are A and B
76. options remaining are A and D
77. options remaining are C and A
78. options remaining are C and A
79. options remaining are B and C
80. options remaining are C and D

9 ♦ ₹12,50,000

1. options remaining are A and D
2. options remaining are C and B
3. options remaining are A and D
4. options remaining are B and C
5. options remaining are B and D
6. options remaining are C and D
7. options remaining are C and D
8. options remaining are A and C
9. options remaining are A and B
10. options remaining are C and D
11. options remaining are C and A
12. options remaining are B and C
13. options remaining are B and C
14. options remaining are A and C
15. options remaining are B and A
16. options remaining are B and A
17. options remaining are C and D
18. options remaining are A and C
19. options remaining are A and D
20. options remaining are B and D
21. options remaining are C and B
22. options remaining are C and A
23. options remaining are C and D
24. options remaining are A and C
25. options remaining are B and A
26. options remaining are A and B
27. options remaining are C and A
28. options remaining are C and D
29. options remaining are B and D
30. options remaining are C and B
31. options remaining are B and A
32. options remaining are A and B
33. options remaining are B and C
34. options remaining are A and B
35. options remaining are B and D
36. options remaining are D and B
37. options remaining are C and B
38. options remaining are C and D
39. options remaining are C and A
40. options remaining are C and D

41. options remaining are A and C
42. options remaining are C and A
43. options remaining are D and B
44. options remaining are C and A
45. options remaining are C and D

10 ♦ ₹25,00,000

1. options remaining are C and A
2. options remaining are A and D
3. options remaining are C and A
4. options remaining are B and C
5. options remaining are D and A
6. options remaining are C and B
7. options remaining are A and C
8. options remaining are C and A
9. options remaining are B and C
10. options remaining are D and B
11. options remaining are D and C
12. options remaining are D and A
13. options remaining are B and C
14. options remaining are C and B
15. options remaining are D and B
16. options remaining are B and C
17. options remaining are A and C
18. options remaining are B and A
19. options remaining are A and D
20. options remaining are D and B
21. options remaining are C and A
22. options remaining are C and A
23. options remaining are D and A
24. options remaining are C and D
25. options remaining are C and A
26. options remaining are B and C
27. options remaining are B and C
28. options remaining are D and A
29. options remaining are D and B
30. options remaining are B and D
31. options remaining are B and C
32. options remaining are A and B
33. options remaining are B and A
34. options remaining are D and C
35. options remaining are B and C
36. options remaining are C and B
37. options remaining are A and C
38. options remaining are B and C
39. options remaining are C and A
40. options remaining are B and C

11 ♦ ₹50,00,000

1. options remaining are D and C
2. options remaining are C and A
3. options remaining are D and A
4. options remaining are C and A
5. options remaining are B and C
6. options remaining are D and B
7. options remaining are D and C
8. options remaining are B and A
9. options remaining are A and B
10. options remaining are D and A
11. options remaining are C and A
12. options remaining are B and A
13. options remaining are D and C
14. options remaining are B and A
15. options remaining are D and A
16. options remaining are C and B
17. options remaining are D and A
18. options remaining are A and D
19. options remaining are A and D
20. options remaining are B and A
21. options remaining are C and A
22. options remaining are A and B
23. options remaining are C and B
24. options remaining are B and D
25. options remaining are C and A
26. options remaining are B and D

27. options remaining are C and B
28. options remaining are B and D
29. options remaining are A and B
30. options remaining are C and A
31. options remaining are D and A
32. options remaining are B and A
33. options remaining are B and D
34. options remaining are A and C
35. options remaining are A and C
36. options remaining are C and D
37. options remaining are C and D
38. options remaining are D and A
39. options remaining are A and B
40. options remaining are C and B

12 ✦ ₹1 Crore

1. options remaining are D and C
2. options remaining are A and C
3. options remaining are A and C
4. options remaining are C and B
5. options remaining are B and D
6. options remaining are C and D
7. options remaining are D and C
8. options remaining are C and A
9. options remaining are C and B
10. options remaining are A and D
11. options remaining are A and D
12. options remaining are C and A
13. options remaining are A and B
14. options remaining are A and C
15. options remaining are A and B
16. options remaining are B and D
17. options remaining are B and C
18. options remaining are D and C
19. options remaining are B and C
20. options remaining are A and C
21. options remaining are B and A
22. options remaining are C and D
23. options remaining are B and C
24. options remaining are C and B
25. options remaining are B and C

Ask the Audience

1 ◆ ₹5,000

1.	A:90%	B:5%	C:0%	D:5%	35.	A:98%	B:0%	C:1%	D:1%
2.	A:0%	B:0%	C:95%	D:5%	36.	A:0%	B:2%	C:95%	D:3%
3.	A:7%	B:0%	C:0%	D:93%	37.	A:0%	B:99%	C:0%	D:1%
4.	A:5%	B:0%	C:3%	D:92%	38.	A:0%	B:98%	C:0%	D:2%
5.	A:0%	B:1%	C:98%	D:1%	39.	A:0%	B:0%	C:0%	D:100%
6.	A:0%	B:100%	C:0%	D:0%	40.	A:0%	B:0%	C:98%	D:2%
7.	A:100%	B:0%	C:0%	D:0%	41.	A:0%	B:0%	C:0%	D:100%
8.	A:98%	B:2%	C:0%	D:0%	42.	A:0%	B:0%	C:2%	D:98%
9.	A:1%	B:0%	C:1%	D:98%	43.	A:0%	B:96%	C:2%	D:2%
10.	A:2%	B:3%	C:94%	D:1%	44.	A:0%	B:0%	C:100%	D:0%
11.	A:0%	B:0%	C:100%	D:0%	45.	A:3%	B:4%	C:93%	D:0%
12.	A:0%	B:0%	C:99%	D:1%	46.	A:0%	B:0%	C:98%	D:2%
13.	A:2%	B:0%	C:2%	D:96%	47.	A:0%	B:100%	C:0%	D:0%
14.	A:99%	B:0%	C:1%	D:0%	48.	A:99%	B:0%	C:1%	D:0%
15.	A:0%	B:0%	C:99%	D:1%	49.	A:0%	B:1%	C:2%	D:97%
16.	A:2%	B:0%	C:98%	D:0%	50.	A:0%	B:0%	C:0%	D:100%
17.	A:1%	B:98%	C:1%	D:0%	51.	A:0%	B:0%	C:0%	D:100%
18.	A:2%	B:0%	C:5%	D:93%	52.	A:5%	B:5%	C:95%	D:0%
19.	A:0%	B:95%	C:0%	D:5%	53.	A:2%	B:0%	C:5%	D:93%
20.	A:0%	B:100%	C:0%	D:0%	54.	A:1%	B:1%	C:98%	D:0%
21.	A:2%	B:0%	C:2%	D:96%	55.	A:0%	B:0%	C:0%	D:100%
22.	A:2%	B:2%	C:96%	D:0%	56.	A:0%	B:98%	C:0%	D:2%
23.	A:0%	B:100%	C:0%	D:0%	57.	A:0%	B:0%	C:98%	D:2%
24.	A:0%	B:93%	C:5%	D:2%	58.	A:0%	B:0%	C:2%	D:98%
25.	A:0%	B:0%	C:1%	D:99%	59.	A:2%	B:3%	C:0%	D:95%
26.	A:0%	B:98%	C:1%	D:1%	60.	A:2%	B:98%	C:0%	D:0%
27.	A:92%	B:4%	C:4%	D:0%	61.	A:98%	B:1%	C:1%	D:0%
28.	A:1%	B:98%	C:1%	D:0%	62.	A:2%	B:98%	C:0%	D:0%
29.	A:0%	B:0%	C:100%	D:0%	63.	A:2%	B:0%	C:98%	D:0%
30.	A:98%	B:0%	C:2%	D:0%	64.	A:0%	B:0%	C:0%	D:100%
31.	A:0%	B:3%	C:0%	D:97%	65.	A:0%	B:98%	C:2%	D:0%
32.	A:1%	B:0%	C:0%	D:99%	66.	A:0%	B:1%	C:99%	D:0%
33.	A:96%	B:0%	C:2%	D:2%	67.	A:2%	B:0%	C:98%	D:0%
34.	A:1%	B:1%	C:98%	D:0%	68.	A:2%	B:0%	C:0%	D:98%

69.	A:0%	B:98%	C:0%	D:2%	95.	A:0%	B:1%	C:98%	D:1%
70.	A:1%	B:1%	C:98%	D:0%	96.	A:0%	B:100%	C:0%	D:0%
71.	A:93%	B:0%	C:5%	D:2%	97.	A:0%	B:99%	C:1%	D:0%
72.	A:2%	B:96%	C:0%	D:2%	98.	A:0%	B:0%	C:2%	D:98%
73.	A:2%	B:98%	C:0%	D:0%	99.	A:2%	B:0%	C:0%	D:98%
74.	A:0%	B:1%	C:99%	D:0%	100.	A:0%	B:0%	C:100%	D:0%
75.	A:97%	B:2%	C:1%	D:0%	101.	A:2%	B:0%	C:98%	D:0%
76.	A:2%	B:0%	C:5%	D:93%	102.	A:2%	B:98%	C:0%	D:0%
77.	A:0%	B:2%	C:98%	D:0%	103.	A:0%	B:0%	C:100%	D:0%
78.	A:2%	B:1%	C:97%	D:0%	104.	A:1%	B:1%	C:0%	D:98%
79.	A:97%	B:2%	C:1%	D:0%	105.	A:0%	B:98%	C:1%	D:1%
80.	A:1%	B:1%	C:98%	D:0%	106.	A:0%	B:0%	C:98%	D:2%
81.	A:2%	B:0%	C:5%	D:93%	107.	A:1%	B:1%	C:98%	D:0%
82.	A:0%	B:0%	C:98%	D:2%	108.	A:1%	B:98%	C:0%	D:1%
83.	A:0%	B:2%	C:0%	D:98%	109.	A:2%	B:98%	C:0%	D:0%
84.	A:0%	B:0%	C:98%	D:2%	110.	A:1%	B:0%	C:98%	D:0%
85.	A:1%	B:98%	C:1%	D:0%	111.	A:2%	B:98%	C:0%	D:0%
86.	A:2%	B:0%	C:97%	D:1%	112.	A:1%	B:1%	C:98%	D:0%
87.	A:0%	B:0%	C:98%	D:2%	113.	A:2%	B:0%	C:96%	D:2%
88.	A:0%	B:0%	C:2%	D:98%	114.	A:2%	B:2%	C:98%	D:0%
89.	A:0%	B:99%	C:1%	D:0%	115.	A:0%	B:98%	C:2%	D:0%
90.	A:0%	B:99%	C:1%	D:0%	116.	A:0%	B:0%	C:2%	D:98%
91.	A:0%	B:0%	C:5%	D:95%	117.	A:2%	B:98%	C:0%	D:0%
92.	A:97%	B:2%	C:1%	D:0%	118.	A:1%	B:0%	C:99%	D:0%
93.	A:0%	B:0%	C:1%	D:99%	119.	A:0%	B:0%	C:0%	D:100%
94.	A:0%	B:99%	C:0%	D:1%	120.	A:0%	B:98%	C:2%	D:0%

2 ♦ ₹10,000

1.	A:1%	B:99%	C:0%	D:0%	15.	A:2%	B:3%	C:92%	D:2%
2.	A:1%	B:0%	C:99%	D:0%	16.	A:2%	B:0%	C:98%	D:0%
3.	A:1%	B:99%	C:0%	D:0%	17.	A:0%	B:2%	C:0%	D:98%
4.	A:0%	B:0%	C:1%	D:99%	18.	A:99%	B:0%	C:1%	D:0%
5.	A:0%	B:98%	C:2%	D:0%	19.	A:0%	B:98%	C:0%	D:2%
6.	A:98%	B:2%	C:0%	D:0%	20.	A:0%	B:1%	C:99%	D:0%
7.	A:2%	B:98%	C:0%	D:0%	21.	A:1%	B:99%	C:0%	D:0%
8.	A:0%	B:95%	C:3%	D:2%	22.	A:0%	B:0%	C:1%	D:99%
9.	A:0%	B:1%	C:99%	D:0%	23.	A:1%	B:99%	C:0%	D:0%
10.	A:0%	B:1%	C:0%	D:99%	24.	A:0%	B:1%	C:99%	D:0%
11.	A:2%	B:3%	C:94%	D:1%	25.	A:0%	B:2%	C:98%	D:0%
12.	A:98%	B:0%	C:0%	D:2%	26.	A:0%	B:0%	C:1%	D:99%
13.	A:1%	B:99%	C:0%	D:0%	27.	A:98%	B:0%	C:0%	D:2%
14.	A:1%	B:99%	C:0%	D:0%	28.	A:98%	B:2%	C:0%	D:0%

29.	A:0%	B:2%	C:0%	D:98%	72.	A:1%	B:0%	C:98%	D:1%
30.	A:2%	B:1%	C:95%	D:2%	73.	A:99%	B:1%	C:0%	D:0%
31.	A:99%	B:0%	C:1%	D:0%	74.	A:0%	B:0%	C:99%	D:1%
32.	A:0%	B:0%	C:99%	D:1%	75.	A:0%	B:2%	C:0%	D:98%
33.	A:0%	B:0%	C:98%	D:2%	76.	A:99%	B:0%	C:0%	D:1%
34.	A:0%	B:99%	C:0%	D:1%	77.	A:98%	B:0%	C:1%	D:1%
35.	A:0%	B:1%	C:99%	D:0%	78.	A:1%	B:0%	C:0%	D:99%
36.	A:1%	B:3%	C:96%	D:0%	79.	A:0%	B:0%	C:100%	D:0%
37.	A:0%	B:99%	C:0%	D:1%	80.	A:0%	B:0%	C:99%	D:1%
38.	A:0%	B:99%	C:0%	D:1%	81.	A:0%	B:0%	C:1%	D:99%
39.	A:0%	B:0%	C:98%	D:2%	82.	A:0%	B:1%	C:0%	D:99%
40.	A:2%	B:98%	C:0%	D:0%	83.	A:0%	B:0%	C:98%	D:2%
41.	A:1%	B:0%	C:99%	D:0%	84.	A:0%	B:1%	C:0%	D:99%
42.	A:99%	B:1%	C:0%	D:0%	85.	A:0%	B:0%	C:99%	D:1%
43.	A:94%	B:1%	C:3%	D:2%	86.	A:1%	B:0%	C:99%	D:0%
44.	A:0%	B:1%	C:0%	D:99%	87.	A:1%	B:98%	C:0%	D:1%
45.	A:0%	B:98%	C:0%	D:2%	88.	A:0%	B:1%	C:99%	D:0%
46.	A:2%	B:0%	C:0%	D:98%	89.	A:98%	B:2%	C:0%	D:0%
47.	A:1%	B:99%	C:0%	D:0%	90.	A:1%	B:2%	C:3%	D:94%
48.	A:2%	B:0%	C:98%	D:0%	91.	A:0%	B:2%	C:98%	D:0%
49.	A:98%	B:2%	C:0%	D:0%	92.	A:1%	B:1%	C:98%	D:0%
50.	A:96%	B:2%	C:1%	D:1%	93.	A:2%	B:2%	C:1%	D:95%
51.	A:0%	B:2%	C:0%	D:98%	94.	A:98%	B:0%	C:0%	D:2%
52.	A:1%	B:99%	C:0%	D:0%	95.	A:2%	B:0%	C:98%	D:0%
53.	A:99%	B:1%	C:0%	D:0%	96.	A:98%	B:0%	C:1%	D:1%
54.	A:2%	B:98%	C:0%	D:0%	97.	A:2%	B:0%	C:1%	D:97%
55.	A:0%	B:0%	C:99%	D:1%	98.	A:2%	B:0%	C:98%	D:0%
56.	A:0%	B:0%	C:1%	D:99%	99.	A:2%	B:98%	C:0%	D:0%
57.	A:0%	B:0%	C:99%	D:1%	100.	A:0%	B:0%	C:2%	D:98%
58.	A:96%	B:4%	C:0%	D:0%	101.	A:0%	B:0%	C:2%	D:98%
59.	A:1%	B:0%	C:99%	D:0%	102.	A:0%	B:2%	C:0%	D:98%
60.	A:0%	B:98%	C:1%	D:1%	103.	A:0%	B:1%	C:98%	D:1%
61.	A:0%	B:0%	C:1%	D:99%	104.	A:0%	B:0%	C:99%	D:1%
62.	A:95%	B:2%	C:2%	D:1%	105.	A:0%	B:0%	C:2%	D:98%
63.	A:0%	B:0%	C:0%	D:100%	106.	A:0%	B:0%	C:99%	D:1%
64.	A:3%	B:0%	C:1%	D:96%	107.	A:1%	B:99%	C:0%	D:0%
65.	A:98%	B:0%	C:2%	D:0%	108.	A:1%	B:99%	C:0%	D:0%
66.	A:2%	B:2%	C:1%	D:95%	109.	A:0%	B:1%	C:0%	D:99%
67.	A:98%	B:0%	C:2%	D:0%	110.	A:1%	B:0%	C:99%	D:0%
68.	A:1%	B:99%	C:0%	D:0%	111.	A:99%	B:0%	C:0%	D:1%
69.	A:0%	B:0%	C:98%	D:2%	112.	A:0%	B:0%	C:97%	D:3%
70.	A:2%	B:0%	C:1%	D:97%	113.	A:0%	B:0%	C:98%	D:2%
71.	A:1%	B:98%	C:0%	D:1%	114.	A:99%	B:0%	C:1%	D:0%

115.	A:2%	B:0%	C:0%	D:98%	118. A:2%	B:0%	C:98%	D:0%
116.	A:99%	B:1%	C:0%	D:0%	119. A:0%	B:0%	C:99%	D:1%
117.	A:2%	B:0%	C:0%	D:98%	120. A:1%	B:99%	C:0%	D:0%

3 ✦ ₹20,000

1.	A:2%	B:98%	C:0%	D:0%	38.	A:6%	B:4%	C:90%	D:0%
2.	A:4%	B:7%	C:0%	D:89%	39.	A:88%	B:5%	C:7%	D:0%
3.	A:0%	B:88%	C:7%	D:5%	40.	A:0%	B:7%	C:88%	D:5%
4.	A:7%	B:7%	C:86%	D:0%	41.	A:0%	B:5%	C:90%	D:5%
5.	A:0%	B:92%	C:0%	D:8%	42.	A:91%	B:0%	C:5%	D:4%
6.	A:10%	B:8%	C:82%	D:0%	43.	A:85%	B:8%	C:0%	D:7%
7.	A:7%	B:86%	C:0%	D:7%	44.	A:0%	B:2%	C:94%	D:4%
8.	A:0%	B:10%	C:90%	D:0%	45.	A:0%	B:6%	C:4%	D:90%
9.	A:10%	B:0%	C:90%	D:0%	46.	A:91%	B:4%	C:5%	D:0%
10.	A:9%	B:89%	C:2%	D:0%	47.	A:88%	B:5%	C:7%	D:0%
11.	A:7%	B:89%	C:0%	D:4%	48.	A:0%	B:2%	C:6%	D:92%
12.	A:90%	B:5%	C:0%	D:5%	49.	A:0%	B:5%	C:93%	D:2%
13.	A:0%	B:0%	C:6%	D:94%	50.	A:0%	B:5%	C:95%	D:0%
14.	A:0%	B:6%	C:87%	D:7%	51.	A:90%	B:4%	C:6%	D:0%
15.	A:1%	B:95%	C:0%	D:4%	52.	A:0%	B:93%	C:7%	D:0%
16.	A:7%	B:88%	C:5%	D:0%	53.	A:9%	B:91%	C:0%	D:0%
17.	A:0%	B:6%	C:90%	D:4%	54.	A:0%	B:7%	C:0%	D:93%
18.	A:0%	B:6%	C:7%	D:87%	55.	A:0%	B:92%	C:6%	D:2%
19.	A:11%	B:0%	C:89%	D:0%	56.	A:0%	B:1%	C:94%	D:5%
20.	A:84%	B:10%	C:6%	D:0%	57.	A:7%	B:0%	C:91%	D:2%
21.	A:0%	B:0%	C:12%	D:88%	58.	A:94%	B:2%	C:4%	D:0%
22.	A:10%	B:87%	C:3%	D:0%	59.	A:0%	B:95%	C:0%	D:5%
23.	A:0%	B:6%	C:89%	D:5%	60.	A:4%	B:5%	C:0%	D:91%
24.	A:0%	B:80%	C:13%	D:7%	61.	A:4%	B:0%	C:7%	D:89%
25.	A:80%	B:0%	C:9%	D:11%	62.	A:3%	B:4%	C:93%	D:0%
26.	A:4%	B:6%	C:0%	D:90%	63.	A:0%	B:4%	C:4%	D:92%
27.	A:8%	B:11%	C:81%	D:0%	64.	A:6%	B:0%	C:94%	D:0%
28.	A:7%	B:0%	C:10%	D:83%	65.	A:0%	B:87%	C:6%	D:7%
29.	A:82%	B:11%	C:7%	D:0%	66.	A:0%	B:89%	C:0%	D:11%
30.	A:7%	B:82%	C:0%	D:11%	67.	A:88%	B:7%	C:0%	D:5%
31.	A:9%	B:7%	C:0%	D:84%	68.	A:0%	B:5%	C:7%	D:88%
32.	A:2%	B:93%	C:5%	D:0%	69.	A:0%	B:4%	C:88%	D:8%
33.	A:0%	B:5%	C:3%	D:92%	70.	A:6%	B:89%	C:5%	D:0%
34.	A:5%	B:0%	C:6%	D:89%	71.	A:7%	B:5%	C:88%	D:0%
35.	A:0%	B:10%	C:90%	D:0%	72.	A:5%	B:4%	C:91%	D:0%
36.	A:91%	B:6%	C:0%	D:3%	73.	A:0%	B:90%	C:6%	D:4%
37.	A:2%	B:0%	C:5%	D:93%	74.	A:4%	B:7%	C:89%	D:0%

75.	A:2%	B:6%	C:92%	D:0%
76.	A:4%	B:5%	C:0%	D:91%
77.	A:0%	B:88%	C:5%	D:7%
78.	A:4%	B:92%	C:0%	D:4%
79.	A:3%	B:3%	C:0%	D:94%
80.	A:6%	B:88%	C:5%	D:0%
81.	A:6%	B:88%	C:6%	D:0%
82.	A:4%	B:6%	C:81%	D:9%
83.	A:91%	B:4%	C:0%	D:5%
84.	A:4%	B:92%	C:0%	D:4%
85.	A:6%	B:0%	C:5%	D:89%
86.	A:0%	B:6%	C:89%	D:5%
87.	A:4%	B:6%	C:0%	D:90%
88.	A:0%	B:4%	C:91%	D:5%
89.	A:0%	B:88%	C:6%	D:6%
90.	A:3%	B:5%	C:92%	D:0%
91.	A:7%	B:4%	C:89%	D:0%
92.	A:0%	B:10%	C:7%	D:83%
93.	A:2%	B:92%	C:0%	D:6%
94.	A:88%	B:7%	C:5%	D:0%
95.	A:3%	B:7%	C:90%	D:0%
96.	A:7%	B:4%	C:5%	D:84%
97.	A:6%	B:90%	C:4%	D:0%
98.	A:91%	B:0%	C:5%	D:4%
99.	A:0%	B:5%	C:7%	D:88%
100.	A:85%	B:7%	C:8%	D:0%

4 ✦ ₹40,000

1.	A:0%	B:9%	C:85%	D:6%
2.	A:89%	B:0%	C:2%	D:9%
3.	A:0%	B:81%	C:9%	D:10%
4.	A:0%	B:7%	C:89%	D:4%
5.	A:9%	B:87%	C:4%	D:0%
6.	A:0%	B:2%	C:12%	D:86%
7.	A:8%	B:0%	C:85%	D:7%
8.	A:7%	B:88%	C:0%	D:5%
9.	A:82%	B:9%	C:0%	D:9%
10.	A:85%	B:5%	C:10%	D:0%
11.	A:90%	B:2%	C:8%	D:0%
12.	A:11%	B:0%	C:80%	D:9%
13.	A:0%	B:2%	C:90%	D:8%
14.	A:0%	B:8%	C:12%	D:80%
15.	A:9%	B:2%	C:0%	D:89%
16.	A:10%	B:8%	C:82%	D:0%
17.	A:8%	B:11%	C:81%	D:0%
18.	A:9%	B:83%	C:0%	D:8%
19.	A:85%	B:0%	C:9%	D:6%
20.	A:8%	B:88%	C:0%	D:4%
21.	A:10%	B:0%	C:81%	D:9%
22.	A:5%	B:0%	C:88%	D:7%
23.	A:78%	B:12%	C:10%	D:0%
24.	A:9%	B:79%	C:12%	D:0%
25.	A:5%	B:11%	C:84%	D:0%
26.	A:12%	B:9%	C:79%	D:0%
27.	A:8%	B:81%	C:0%	D:11%
28.	A:6%	B:5%	C:89%	D:0%
29.	A:11%	B:87%	C:0%	D:2%
30.	A:0%	B:8%	C:7%	D:85%
31.	A:5%	B:9%	C:0%	D:86%
32.	A:7%	B:91%	C:0%	D:2%
33.	A:0%	B:87%	C:7%	D:6%
34.	A:81%	B:0%	C:9%	D:10%
35.	A:0%	B:11%	C:81%	D:8%
36.	A:9%	B:71%	C:11%	D:9%
37.	A:9%	B:0%	C:83%	D:8%
38.	A:80%	B:0%	C:12%	D:8%
39.	A:89%	B:8%	C:0%	D:3%
40.	A:9%	B:85%	C:0%	D:6%
41.	A:0%	B:84%	C:10%	D:6%
42.	A:5%	B:11%	C:0%	D:84%
43.	A:8%	B:3%	C:89%	D:0%
44.	A:11%	B:79%	C:10%	D:0%
45.	A:87%	B:7%	C:6%	D:0%
46.	A:4%	B:8%	C:0%	D:88%
47.	A:6%	B:0%	C:7%	D:87%
48.	A:79%	B:0%	C:9%	D:12%
49.	A:0%	B:9%	C:12%	D:79%
50.	A:9%	B:0%	C:8%	D:83%
51.	A:9%	B:80%	C:11%	D:0%
52.	A:12%	B:0%	C:79%	D:9%
53.	A:0%	B:76%	C:10%	D:14%
54.	A:8%	B:76%	C:7%	D:9%

55.	A:0%	B:8%	C:78%	D:14%
56.	A:11%	B:0%	C:80%	D:9%
57.	A:6%	B:81%	C:0%	D:13%
58.	A:0%	B:80%	C:9%	D:11%
59.	A:10%	B:11%	C:79%	D:0%
60.	A:11%	B:78%	C:11%	D:0%
61.	A:10%	B:78%	C:0%	D:12%
62.	A:10%	B:11%	C:0%	D:79%
63.	A:0%	B:9%	C:79%	D:12%
64.	A:0%	B:14%	C:78%	D:8%
65.	A:78%	B:0%	C:12%	D:10%
66.	A:0%	B:13%	C:80%	D:7%
67.	A:7%	B:8%	C:76%	D:9%
68.	A:79%	B:0%	C:12%	D:9%
69.	A:0%	B:73%	C:11%	D:16%
70.	A:8%	B:74%	C:9%	D:9%
71.	A:85%	B:8%	C:0%	D:7%
72.	A:72%	B:18%	C:10%	D:0%
73.	A:9%	B:83%	C:0%	D:8%
74.	A:0%	B:81%	C:8%	D:11%
75.	A:6%	B:0%	C:11%	D:83%
76.	A:12%	B:0%	C:8%	D:80%
77.	A:79%	B:9%	C:12%	D:0%
78.	A:11%	B:80%	C:0%	D:9%
79.	A:0%	B:4%	C:14%	D:82%
80.	A:11%	B:0%	C:8%	D:81%
81.	A:86%	B:7%	C:7%	D:0%
82.	A:0%	B:9%	C:12%	D:79%
83.	A:0%	B:78%	C:11%	D:11%
84.	A:76%	B:12%	C:0%	D:12%
85.	A:9%	B:0%	C:86%	D:5%
86.	A:0%	B:84%	C:3%	D:13%
87.	A:0%	B:9%	C:81%	D:10%
88.	A:75%	B:0%	C:11%	D:14%
89.	A:0%	B:84%	C:9%	D:7%
90.	A:0%	B:10%	C:9%	D:81%

5 ♦ ₹80,000

1.	A:0%	B:11%	C:14%	D:75%
2.	A:10%	B:75%	C:5%	D:10%
3.	A:11%	B:10%	C:70%	D:9%
4.	A:74%	B:16%	C:10%	D:0%
5.	A:9%	B:72%	C:12%	D:7%
6.	A:76%	B:14%	C:10%	D:0%
7.	A:72%	B:12%	C:10%	D:6%
8.	A:0%	B:10%	C:12%	D:78%
9.	A:12%	B:76%	C:12%	D:0%
10.	A:0%	B:81%	C:11%	D:8%
11.	A:60%	B:18%	C:12%	D:10%
12.	A:72%	B:15%	C:13%	D:0%
13.	A:0%	B:7%	C:14%	D:79%
14.	A:0%	B:82%	C:8%	D:10%
15.	A:79%	B:12%	C:0%	D:9%
16.	A:9%	B:0%	C:8%	D:83%
17.	A:81%	B:12%	C:7%	D:0%
18.	A:14%	B:79%	C:0%	D:7%
19.	A:0%	B:9%	C:89%	D:11%
20.	A:0%	B:10%	C:72%	D:18%
21.	A:9%	B:0%	C:9%	D:82%
22.	A:14%	B:74%	C:12%	D:0%
23.	A:0%	B:86%	C:9%	D:5%
24.	A:81%	B:8%	C:0%	D:11%
25.	A:0%	B:4%	C:88%	D:8%
26.	A:11%	B:10%	C:0%	D:79%
27.	A:4%	B:10%	C:77%	D:9%
28.	A:79%	B:12%	C:9%	D:0%
29.	A:0%	B:10%	C:12%	D:78%
30.	A:0%	B:79%	C:10%	D:11%
31.	A:12%	B:77%	C:0%	D:11%
32.	A:15%	B:76%	C:9%	D:0%
33.	A:0%	B:10%	C:14%	D:76%
34.	A:0%	B:14%	C:74%	D:12%
35.	A:0%	B:12%	C:72%	D:16%
36.	A:11%	B:79%	C:10%	D:0%
37.	A:13%	B:74%	C:13%	D:0%
38.	A:0%	B:14%	C:10%	D:76%
39.	A:0%	B:10%	C:15%	D:75%
40.	A:79%	B:12%	C:9%	D:0%
41.	A:6%	B:86%	C:8%	D:0%
42.	A:12%	B:0%	C:76%	D:12%
43.	A:12%	B:78%	C:10%	D:0%
44.	A:15%	B:0%	C:14%	D:71%

45.	A:5%	B:9%	C:10%	D:76%
46.	A:10%	B:76%	C:14%	D:0%
47.	A:0%	B:12%	C:76%	D:12%
48.	A:81%	B:11%	C:8%	D:0%
49.	A:11%	B:72%	C:5%	D:12%
50.	A:9%	B:10%	C:72%	D:9%
51.	A:10%	B:0%	C:12%	D:78%
52.	A:79%	B:12%	C:9%	D:0%
53.	A:4%	B:87%	C:9%	D:0%
54.	A:72%	B:12%	C:10%	D:6%
55.	A:10%	B:79%	C:11%	D:0%
56.	A:0%	B:79%	C:10%	D:11%
57.	A:0%	B:81%	C:10%	D:9%
58.	A:7%	B:0%	C:12%	D:81%
59.	A:5%	B:14%	C:81%	D:0%
60.	A:14%	B:73%	C:0%	D:13%
61.	A:82%	B:10%	C:8%	D:0%
62.	A:74%	B:10%	C:16%	D:0%
63.	A:0%	B:9%	C:81%	D:10%
64.	A:9%	B:81%	C:10%	D:0%
65.	A:9%	B:0%	C:81%	D:10%
66.	A:8%	B:0%	C:86%	D:6%
67.	A:13%	B:10%	C:14%	D:63%
68.	A:5%	B:85%	C:10%	D:0%
69.	A:12%	B:0%	C:76%	D:12%
70.	A:76%	B:14%	C:0%	D:10%
71.	A:0%	B:72%	C:13%	D:15%
72.	A:9%	B:81%	C:0%	D:10%
73.	A:5%	B:86%	C:9%	D:0%
74.	A:5%	B:0%	C:6%	D:89%
75.	A:6%	B:9%	C:85%	D:0%
76.	A:14%	B:0%	C:10%	D:76%
77.	A:8%	B:10%	C:0%	D:82%
78.	A:11%	B:79%	C:10%	D:0%
79.	A:7%	B:0%	C:12%	D:81%
80.	A:6%	B:0%	C:86%	D:8%

6 ◆ ₹1,60,000

1.	A:12%	B:79%	C:9%	D:0%
2.	A:0%	B:81%	C:11%	D:8%
3.	A:0%	B:11%	C:79%	D:10%
4.	A:12%	B:72%	C:11%	D:5%
5.	A:12%	B:76%	C:12%	D:0%
6.	A:10%	B:9%	C:81%	D:0%
7.	A:12%	B:0%	C:9%	D:79%
8.	A:9%	B:10%	C:81%	D:0%
9.	A:79%	B:0%	C:10%	D:11%
10.	A:2%	B:9%	C:8%	D:81%
11.	A:0%	B:12%	C:79%	D:9%
12.	A:0%	B:12%	C:12%	D:76%
13.	A:0%	B:11%	C:78%	D:11%
14.	A:7%	B:9%	C:0%	D:84%
15.	A:8%	B:88%	C:4%	D:0%
16.	A:79%	B:14%	C:7%	D:0%
17.	A:3%	B:11%	C:86%	D:0%
18.	A:57%	B:12%	C:14%	D:17%
19.	A:0%	B:9%	C:10%	D:81%
20.	A:9%	B:72%	C:10%	D:9%
21.	A:6%	B:10%	C:84%	D:0%
22.	A:0%	B:14%	C:72%	D:14%
23.	A:76%	B:0%	C:15%	D:9%
24.	A:10%	B:0%	C:12%	D:78%
25.	A:76%	B:11%	C:8%	D:5%
26.	A:0%	B:9%	C:81%	D:10%
27.	A:12%	B:0%	C:79%	D:9%
28.	A:9%	B:11%	C:80%	D:0%
29.	A:0%	B:7%	C:9%	D:84%
30.	A:9%	B:79%	C:8%	D:4%
31.	A:11%	B:8%	C:81%	D:0%
32.	A:0%	B:12%	C:12%	D:76%
33.	A:10%	B:81%	C:9%	D:0%
34.	A:0%	B:12%	C:6%	D:82%
35.	A:10%	B:79%	C:11%	D:0%
36.	A:3%	B:12%	C:11%	D:74%
37.	A:16%	B:76%	C:0%	D:8%
38.	A:13%	B:0%	C:12%	D:75%
39.	A:7%	B:84%	C:0%	D:9%
40.	A:81%	B:9%	C:0%	D:10%
41.	A:72%	B:12%	C:9%	D:7%
42.	A:13%	B:0%	C:12%	D:75%
43.	A:9%	B:9%	C:11%	D:71%
44.	A:13%	B:78%	C:0%	D:9%

45.	A:16%	B:0%	C:72%	D:12%
46.	A:79%	B:0%	C:11%	D:10%
47.	A:74%	B:14%	C:12%	D:0%
48.	A:0%	B:12%	C:12%	D:76%
49.	A:12%	B:0%	C:74%	D:14%
50.	A:0%	B:81%	C:12%	D:7%
51.	A:0%	B:11%	C:84%	D:5%
52.	A:0%	B:11%	C:8%	D:81%
53.	A:7%	B:11%	C:74%	D:8%
54.	A:11%	B:14%	C:71%	D:4%
55.	A:10%	B:79%	C:11%	D:0%
56.	A:11%	B:78%	C:11%	D:0%
57.	A:81%	B:11%	C:8%	D:0%
58.	A:79%	B:9%	C:7%	D:5%
59.	A:0%	B:10%	C:12%	D:78%
60.	A:11%	B:81%	C:8%	D:0%
61.	A:5%	B:11%	C:0%	D:84%
62.	A:74%	B:9%	C:0%	D:17%
63.	A:0%	B:11%	C:82%	D:7%
64.	A:9%	B:84%	C:0%	D:7%
65.	A:0%	B:79%	C:12%	D:9%
66.	A:0%	B:12%	C:77%	D:11%
67.	A:0%	B:16%	C:74%	D:10%
68.	A:17%	B:71%	C:12%	D:0%
69.	A:79%	B:11%	C:10%	D:0%
70.	A:9%	B:79%	C:0%	D:12%
71.	A:0%	B:12%	C:14%	D:74%
72.	A:14%	B:71%	C:0%	D:15%
73.	A:10%	B:71%	C:19%	D:0%
74.	A:0%	B:12%	C:74%	D:14%
75.	A:4%	B:13%	C:11%	D:72%
76.	A:7%	B:0%	C:8%	D:85%
77.	A:6%	B:74%	C:11%	D:9%
78.	A:79%	B:12%	C:0%	D:9%
79.	A:8%	B:76%	C:9%	D:7%
80.	A:14%	B:74%	C:0%	D:12%

7 ✦ ₹3,20,000

1	A:32%	B:37%	C:14%	D:17%
2.	A:17%	B:12%	C:30%	D:41%
3.	A:20%	B:44%	C:11%	D:25%
4.	A:30%	B:15%	C:30%	D:25%
5.	A:38%	B:15%	C:17%	D:30%
6.	A:10%	B:60%	C:15%	D:15%
7.	A:37%	B:19%	C:37%	D:7%
8.	A:20%	B:48%	C:15%	D:17%
9.	A:17%	B:49%	C:21%	D:13%
10.	A:15%	B:19%	C:20%	D:46%
11.	A:35%	B:22%	C:34%	D:9%
12.	A:31%	B:16%	C:37%	D:16%
13.	A:5%	B:17%	C:59%	D:19%
14.	A:35%	B:17%	C:18%	D:30%
15.	A:0%	B:64%	C:22%	D:14%
16.	A:14%	B:14%	C:29%	D:43%
17.	A:24%	B:20%	C:12%	D:44%
18.	A:13%	B:24%	C:10%	D:53%
19.	A:11%	B:5%	C:69%	D:15%
20.	A:12%	B:55%	C:14%	D:19%
21.	A:5%	B:25%	C:55%	D:15%
22.	A:33%	B:29%	C:17%	D:21%
23.	A:67%	B:2%	C:16%	D:15%
24.	A:18%	B:50%	C:18%	D:14%
25.	A:48%	B:14%	C:17%	D:21%
26.	A:26%	B:26%	C:29%	D:19%
27.	A:6%	B:63%	C:17%	D:14%
28.	A:21%	B:24%	C:23%	D:32%
29.	A:29%	B:21%	C:19%	D:31%
30.	A:49%	B:11%	C:16%	D:24%
31.	A:15%	B:58%	C:17%	D:10%
32.	A:31%	B:21%	C:17%	D:31%
33.	A:18%	B:5%	C:59%	D:18%
34.	A:16%	B:70%	C:1%	D:13%
35.	A:44%	B:18%	C:20%	D:18%
36.	A:30%	B:31%	C:21%	D:18%
37.	A:17%	B:28%	C:38%	D:17%
38.	A:18%	B:24%	C:33%	D:25%
39.	A:46%	B:14%	C:14%	D:26%
40.	A:49%	B:19%	C:15%	D:17%
41.	A:11%	B:15%	C:60%	D:14%
42.	A:37%	B:35%	C:26%	D:2%

43.	A:70%	B:16%	C:14%	D:0%
44.	A:23%	B:35%	C:23%	D:19%
45.	A:10%	B:61%	C:14%	D:15%
46.	A:14%	B:17%	C:69%	D:0%
47.	A:42%	B:36%	C:12%	D:10%
48.	A:0%	B:19%	C:67%	D:14%
49.	A:28%	B:47%	C:14%	D:11%
50.	A:18%	B:20%	C:51%	D:11%
51.	A:62%	B:17%	C:14%	D:7%
52.	A:17%	B:51%	C:21%	D:13%
53.	A:18%	B:13%	C:0%	D:69%
54.	A:0%	B:25%	C:47%	D:28%
55.	A:21%	B:51%	C:16%	D:12%
56.	A:27%	B:21%	C:14%	D:38%
57.	A:19%	B:19%	C:14%	D:48%
58.	A:14%	B:17%	C:68%	D:1%
59.	A:18%	B:22%	C:49%	D:11%
60.	A:39%	B:18%	C:25%	D:18%
61.	A:13%	B:17%	C:60%	D:10%
62.	A:16%	B:16%	C:53%	D:15%
63.	A:13%	B:70%	C:17%	D:0%
64.	A:35%	B:22%	C:26%	D:17%
65.	A:21%	B:35%	C:25%	D:19%
66.	A:16%	B:18%	C:52%	D:14%
67.	A:16%	B:14%	C:10%	D:60%
68.	A:43%	B:22%	C:32%	D:3%
69.	A:14%	B:2%	C:67%	D:17%
70.	A:28%	B:33%	C:26%	D:13%
71.	A:12%	B:0%	C:71%	D:17%
72.	A:34%	B:33%	C:16%	D:17%
73.	A:18%	B:52%	C:16%	D:14%
74.	A:22%	B:26%	C:38%	D:14%
75.	A:17%	B:68%	C:1%	D:14%
76.	A:10%	B:58%	C:19%	D:13%
77.	A:14%	B:38%	C:28%	D:20%
78.	A:39%	B:12%	C:23%	D:26%
79.	A:26%	B:16%	C:40%	D:18%
80.	A:17%	B:3%	C:12%	D:68%

8 ♦ ₹6,40,000

1	A:14%	B:17%	C:62%	D:7%
2.	A:11%	B:65%	C:5%	D:19%
3.	A:23%	B:15%	C:47%	D:15%
4.	A:37%	B:0%	C:41%	D:22%
5.	A:19%	B:18%	C:24%	D:39%
6.	A:64%	B:12%	C:7%	D:17%
7.	A:12%	B:14%	C:58%	D:16%
8.	A:2%	B:12%	C:70%	D:16%
9.	A:19%	B:40%	C:12%	D:29%
10.	A:21%	B:19%	C:40%	D:20%
11.	A:16%	B:33%	C:39%	D:12%
12.	A:41%	B:11%	C:28%	D:20%
13.	A:24%	B:19%	C:12%	D:45%
14.	A:12%	B:20%	C:59%	D:9%
15.	A:14%	B:34%	C:35%	D:17%
16.	A:18%	B:11%	C:60%	D:11%
17.	A:20%	B:36%	C:20%	D:24%
18.	A:35%	B:18%	C:37%	D:10%
19.	A:15%	B:62%	C:14%	D:9%
20.	A:29%	B:5%	C:19%	D:47%
21.	A:23%	B:27%	C:30%	D:20%
22.	A:9%	B:17%	C:54%	D:20%
23.	A:51%	B:9%	C:10%	D:30%
24.	A:32%	B:32%	C:26%	D:10%
25.	A:19%	B:8%	C:22%	D:51%
26.	A:20%	B:49%	C:14%	D:17%
27.	A:12%	B:62%	C:8%	D:18%
28.	A:25%	B:35%	C:24%	D:16%
29.	A:11%	B:19%	C:17%	D:53%
30.	A:12%	B:47%	C:29%	D:12%
31.	A:11%	B:24%	C:35%	D:30%
32.	A:12%	B:3%	C:20%	D:65%
33.	A:43%	B:23%	C:16%	D:18%
34.	A:17%	B:42%	C:18%	D:23%
35.	A:23%	B:21%	C:37%	D:19%
36.	A:22%	B:24%	C:21%	D:33%
37.	A:12%	B:4%	C:66%	D:18%
38.	A:11%	B:56%	C:13%	D:20%
39.	A:15%	B:64%	C:10%	D:11%
40.	A:5%	B:23%	C:63%	D:9%
41.	A:13%	B:18%	C:49%	D:20%
42.	A:10%	B:13%	C:67%	D:10%

43.	A:15%	B:46%	C:21%	D:18%
44.	A:12%	B:21%	C:32%	D:35%
45.	A:9%	B:8%	C:80%	D:3%
46.	A:14%	B:43%	C:20%	D:23%
47.	A:27%	B:21%	C:28%	D:24%
48.	A:8%	B:59%	C:11%	D:22%
49.	A:12%	B:11%	C:32%	D:45%
50.	A:61%	B:9%	C:20%	D:10%
51.	A:22%	B:34%	C:21%	D:23%
52.	A:23%	B:19%	C:20%	D:38%
53.	A:13%	B:39%	C:19%	D:29%
54.	A:11%	B:19%	C:23%	D:47%
55.	A:9%	B:49%	C:29%	D:13%
56.	A:39%	B:15%	C:18%	D:28%
57.	A:24%	B:33%	C:8%	D:35%
58.	A:29%	B:18%	C:34%	D:19%
59.	A:21%	B:27%	C:28%	D:24%
60.	A:18%	B:41%	C:18%	D:23%
61.	A:17%	B:40%	C:25%	D:18%
62.	A:17%	B:36%	C:45%	D:2%
63.	A:3%	B:20%	C:18%	D:59%
64.	A:18%	B:20%	C:48%	D:14%
65.	A:11%	B:56%	C:12%	D:21%
66.	A:12%	B:58%	C:19%	D:11%
67.	A:20%	B:13%	C:16%	D:51%
68.	A:19%	B:6%	C:67%	D:8%
69.	A:65%	B:10%	C:11%	D:14%
70.	A:13%	B:18%	C:26%	D:43%
71.	A:12%	B:45%	C:39%	D:4%
72.	A:56%	B:11%	C:20%	D:13%
73.	A:8%	B:11%	C:60%	D:21%
74.	A:31%	B:23%	C:19%	D:27%
75.	A:43%	B:18%	C:17%	D:22%
76.	A:49%	B:20%	C:19%	D:12%
77.	A:16%	B:18%	C:41%	D:25%
78.	A:25%	B:26%	C:25%	D:24%
79.	A:10%	B:49%	C:30%	D:11%
80.	A:18%	B:17%	C:45%	D:20%

9 ✦ ₹12,50,000

1.	A:31%	B:21%	C:30%	D:18%
2.	A:25%	B:20%	C:35%	D:20%
3.	A:27%	B:20%	C:29%	D:24%
4.	A:22%	B:26%	C:28%	D:24%
5.	A:20%	B:30%	C:25%	D:25%
6.	A:30%	B:11%	C:37%	D:22%
7.	A:32%	B:19%	C:39%	D:10%
8.	A:41%	B:15%	C:29%	D:15%
9.	A:27%	B:27%	C:22%	D:24%
10.	A:11%	B:33%	C:30%	D:26%
11.	A:18%	B:19%	C:43%	D:20%
12.	A:25%	B:24%	C:29%	D:22%
13.	A:22%	B:27%	C:24%	D:27%
14.	A:48%	B:10%	C:20%	D:22%
15.	A:20%	B:28%	C:21%	D:31%
16.	A:24%	B:25%	C:21%	D:30%
17.	A:24%	B:27%	C:27%	D:22%
18.	A:28%	B:22%	C:26%	D:24%
19.	A:38%	B:13%	C:23%	D:26%
20.	A:24%	B:27%	C:22%	D:27%
21.	A:27%	B:24%	C:27%	D:22%
22.	A:30%	B:13%	C:35%	D:22%
23.	A:25%	B:24%	C:27%	D:24%
24.	A:28%	B:22%	C:27%	D:23%
25.	A:24%	B:24%	C:27%	D:25%
26.	A:27%	B:43%	C:17%	D:13%
27.	A:31%	B:22%	C:24%	D:23%
28.	A:11%	B:24%	C:43%	D:22%
29.	A:11%	B:34%	C:31%	D:24%
30.	A:26%	B:24%	C:23%	D:27%
31.	A:21%	B:22%	C:29%	D:28%
32.	A:27%	B:22%	C:27%	D:24%
33.	A:26%	B:26%	C:21%	D:27%
34.	A:27%	B:22%	C:26%	D:25%
35.	A:47%	B:17%	C:14%	D:22%
36.	A:24%	B:24%	C:27%	D:25%
37.	A:24%	B:27%	C:22%	D:27%
38.	A:21%	B:21%	C:28%	D:30%
39.	A:30%	B:23%	C:12%	D:35%
40.	A:32%	B:14%	C:45%	D:9%

41.	A:68%	B:2%	C:23%	D:7%
42.	A:5%	B:22%	C:72%	D:1%
43.	A:21%	B:22%	C:11%	D:46%
44.	A:10%	B:24%	C:64%	D:2%
45.	A:3%	B:10%	C:51%	D:36%

10 ♦ ₹25,00,000

1.	A:17%	B:24%	C:30%	D:29%
2.	A:29%	B:24%	C:22%	D:25%
3.	A:25%	B:24%	C:24%	D:27%
4.	A:24%	B:30%	C:27%	D:19%
5.	A:19%	B:27%	C:26%	D:28%
6.	A:24%	B:25%	C:26%	D:25%
7.	A:28%	B:22%	C:28%	D:22%
8.	A:22%	B:24%	C:27%	D:27%
9.	A:18%	B:32%	C:20%	D:30%
10.	A:23%	B:27%	C:22%	D:28%
11.	A:25%	B:27%	C:24%	D:24%
12.	A:22%	B:27%	C:24%	D:27%
13.	A:25%	B:30%	C:24%	D:22%
14.	A:27%	B:27%	C:27%	D:19%
15.	A:28%	B:25%	C:23%	D:24%
16.	A:23%	B:30%	C:23%	D:24%
17.	A:25%	B:28%	C:22%	D:25%
18.	A:23%	B:23%	C:24%	D:30%
19.	A:24%	B:22%	C:27%	D:27%
20.	A:24%	B:24%	C:25%	D:27%
21.	A:29%	B:22%	C:27%	D:22%
22.	A:27%	B:22%	C:29%	D:22%
23.	A:29%	B:22%	C:21%	D:28%
24.	A:27%	B:22%	C:28%	D:23%
25.	A:24%	B:25%	C:27%	D:24%
26.	A:30%	B:28%	C:22%	D:20%
27.	A:22%	B:28%	C:28%	D:22%
28.	A:23%	B:24%	C:22%	D:31%
29.	A:24%	B:24%	C:25%	D:27%
30.	A:28%	B:27%	C:20%	D:25%
31.	A:28%	B:26%	C:22%	D:24%
32.	A:31%	B:22%	C:21%	D:26%
33.	A:19%	B:27%	C:24%	D:30%
34.	A:25%	B:20%	C:30%	D:25%
35.	A:28%	B:27%	C:24%	D:21%
36.	A:27%	B:22%	C:25%	D:26%
37.	A:28%	B:24%	C:26%	D:22%
38.	A:23%	B:32%	C:22%	D:23%
39.	A:23%	B:24%	C:28%	D:25%
40.	A:25%	B:32%	C:20%	D:23%

11 ♦ ₹50,00,000

1.	A:27%	B:24%	C:23%	D:26%
2.	A:26%	B:22%	C:26%	D:26%
3.	A:22%	B:27%	C:24%	D:27%
4.	A:26%	B:24%	C:26%	D:24%
5.	A:26%	B:25%	C:23%	D:26%
6.	A:28%	B:24%	C:24%	D:24%
7.	A:24%	B:24%	C:25%	D:27%
8.	A:24%	B:26%	C:26%	D:24%
9.	A:27%	B:23%	C:24%	D:26%
10.	A:23%	B:28%	C:22%	D:27%
11.	A:27%	B:25%	C:27%	D:21%
12.	A:22%	B:28%	C:27%	D:23%
13.	A:24%	B:26%	C:26%	D:24%
14.	A:24%	B:26%	C:25%	D:25%
15.	A:26%	B:25%	C:25%	D:24%
16.	A:27%	B:24%	C:27%	D:22%
17.	A:26%	B:24%	C:25%	D:25%
18.	A:27%	B:23%	C:27%	D:23%
19.	A:27%	B:26%	C:22%	D:25%
20.	A:24%	B:26%	C:24%	D:26%
21.	A:25%	B:24%	C:27%	D:24%
22.	A:26%	B:27%	C:27%	D:20%
23.	A:23%	B:25%	C:26%	D:26%
24.	A:23%	B:26%	C:27%	D:24%
25.	A:25%	B:23%	C:27%	D:25%
26.	A:23%	B:24%	C:27%	D:26%

27.	A:25%	B:24%	C:27%	D:24%
28.	A:24%	B:25%	C:27%	D:24%
29.	A:28%	B:22%	C:28%	D:22%
30.	A:27%	B:23%	C:23%	D:27%
31.	A:27%	B:24%	C:23%	D:26%
32.	A:24%	B:27%	C:24%	D:25%
33.	A:24%	B:27%	C:20%	D:29%
34.	A:27%	B:25%	C:24%	D:24%
35.	A:27%	B:23%	C:24%	D:26%
36.	A:24%	B:24%	C:26%	D:26%
37.	A:24%	B:24%	C:28%	D:24%
38.	A:27%	B:24%	C:22%	D:27%
39.	A:27%	B:27%	C:24%	D:22%
40.	A:27%	B:27%	C:25%	D:21%

12 ♦ ₹1 Crore

1.	A:25%	B:28%	C:19%	D:28%
2.	A:20%	B:24%	C:32%	D:24%
3.	A:26%	B:24%	C:26%	D:24%
4.	A:28%	B:25%	C:22%	D:25%
5.	A:27%	B:22%	C:23%	D:28%
6.	A:27%	B:26%	C:24%	D:23%
7.	A:26%	B:26%	C:24%	D:24%
8.	A:26%	B:24%	C:25%	D:25%
9.	A:27%	B:25%	C:22%	D:26%
10.	A:27%	B:24%	C:22%	D:27%
11.	A:22%	B:21%	C:28%	D:29%
12.	A:22%	B:24%	C:25%	D:29%
13.	A:24%	B:27%	C:25%	D:24%
14.	A:27%	B:22%	C:27%	D:24%
15.	A:27%	B:28%	C:17%	D:28%
16.	A:24%	B:28%	C:20%	D:28%
17.	A:25%	B:24%	C:26%	D:25%
18.	A:25%	B:27%	C:22%	D:26%
19.	A:22%	B:28%	C:24%	D:26%
20.	A:24%	B:29%	C:24%	D:23%
21.	A:24%	B:27%	C:25%	D:24%
22.	A:28%	B:24%	C:24%	D:24%
23.	A:22%	B:28%	C:28%	D:22%
24.	A:27%	B:25%	C:27%	D:21%
25.	A:26%	B:25%	C:25%	D:24%

Answers

Fastest Finger First

1. ACDB	26. BACD	51. CDBA	76. BCAD
2. BCDA	27. BACD	52. BCDA	77. ACDB
3. CADB	28. DACB	53. CBDA	78. DBCA
4. CABD	29 CABD	54. DACB	79. CADB
5. ACBD	30. BADC	55. BDAC	80. CABD
6. BADC	31. CDAB	56. BADC	81. CABD
7. CADB	32. BACD	57. DBCA	82. BCDA
8. ADCB	33. CBDA	58. BADC	83. BACD
9. BACD	34. DBAC	59. ACDB	84. DBAC
10. ABCD	35. CBAD	60. BCAD	85. DCAB
11. CBAD	36. ACBD	61. DBCA	86. ACBD
12. ACBD	37. ACBD	62. CADB	87. CBAD
13. ADCB	38. BDAC	63. BCDA	88. DBCA
14. CBDA	39. BADC	64. BACD	89. ADCB
15. BDCA	40. ADCB	65. CADB	90. CABD
16. BDCA	41. BCAD	66. BDAC	91. ADCB
17. BDCA	42. BCAD	67. ABDC	92. BADC
18. BCAD	43. ACDB	68. BACD	93. BDCA
19. BADC	44. DABC	69. ACDB	94. CBAD
20. CADB	45. CABD	70. CADB	95. BDCA
21. DACB	46. BDCA	71. ACBD	96. BDAC
22. CDAB	47. CABD	72. BDAC	97. BCDA
23. ABDC	48. DBCA	73. BDAC	98. CBAD
24. ADCB	49. DBCA	74. DACB	99. BDCA
25. BDCA	50. BCDA	75. DACB	100. DBCA

If you answered correctly, well done! Turn to page 1 to play for ₹5,000

1 ♦ ₹5,000

1. A	6. B	11. C	16. C
2. C	7. A	12. C	17. B
3. D	8. A	13. D	18. D
4. D	9. D	14. A	19. B
5. C	10. C	15. C	20. B

21. D	46. C	71. A	96 B
22. C	47. B	72. B	97 B
23. B	48. A	73. B	98 D
24. B	49. D	74 C	99 D
25. D	50. D	75 A	100 C
26. B	51. D	76 D	101 C
27. A	52. C	77 C	102 B
28. B	53. D	78 C	103 C
29. C	54. C	79 A	104 D
30. A	55. D	80 C	105 B
31. D	56. B	81 D	106 C
32. D	57. C	82 C	107 C
33. A	58. D	83 D	108 B
34. C	59. D	84 C	109 B
35. A	60. B	85 B	110 C
36. C	61. A	86 C	111 B
37. B	62. B	87 C	112 C
38. B	63. C	88 D	113 C
39. D	64. D	89 B	114 C
40. C	65. B	90 B	115 B
41. D	66. C	91 D	116 D
42. D	67. C	92 A	117 B
43. B	68. D	93 D	118 C
44. C	69. B	94 B	119 D
45. C	70. C	95 C	120 B

2 ♦ ₹10,000

1 B	16 C	31 A	46 D
2 C	17 D	32 C	47 B
3 B	18 A	33 C	48 C
4 D	19 B	34 B	49 A
5 B	20 C	35 C	50 A
6 A	21 B	36 C	51 D
7 B	22 D	37 B	52 B
8 B	23 B	38 B	53 A
9 C	24 C	39 C	54 B
10 D	25 C	40 B	55 C
11 C	26 D	41 C	56 D
12 A	27 A	42 A	57 C
13 B	28 A	43 A	58 A
14 B	29 D	44 D	59 C
15 C	30 C	45 B	60 B

61	D	76	A	91	C	106	C
62	A	77	A	92	C	107	B
63	D	78	D	93	D	108	B
64	D	79	C	94	A	109	D
65	A	80	C	95	C	110	C
66	D	81	D	96	A	111	A
67	A	82	D	97	D	112	C
68	B	83	C	98	C	113	C
69	C	84	D	99	B	114	A
70	D	85	C	100	D	115	D
71	B	86	C	101	D	116	A
72	C	87	B	102	D	117	D
73	A	88	C	103	C	118	C
74	C	89	A	104	C	119	C
75	D	90	D	105	D	120	B

3 ♦ ₹20,000

1	B	26	D	51	A	76	D
2	D	27	C	52	B	77	B
3	B	28	D	53	B	78	B
4	C	29	A	54	D	79	D
5	B	30	B	55	B	80	B
6	C	31	D	56	C	81	B
7	B	32	B	57	C	82	C
8	C	33	D	58	A	83	A
9	C	34	D	59	B	84	B
10	B	35	C	60	D	85	D
11	B	36	A	61	D	86	C
12	A	37	D	62	C	87	D
13	D	38	C	63	D	88	C
14	C	39	A	64	C	89	B
15	B	40	C	65	B	90	C
16	B	41	B	66	B	91	C
17	C	42	A	67	A	92	D
18	D	43	A	68	D	93	B
19	C	44	C	69	C	94	A
20	A	45	D	70	B	95	C
21	D	46	A	71	C	96	D
22	B	47	A	72	C	97	B
23	C	48	D	73	B	98	A
24	B	49	C	74	C	99	D
25	A	50	C	75	C	100	A

4 ♦ ₹40,000

1	C	24	B	47	D	70	B
2	A	25	C	48	A	71	A
3	B	26	C	49	D	72	A
4	C	27	B	50	D	73	B
5	B	28	C	51	B	74	B
6	D	29	B	52	C	75	D
7	C	30	D	53	B	76	D
8	B	31	D	54	B	77	A
9	A	32	B	55	C	78	B
10	A	33	B	56	C	79	D
11	A	34	A	57	B	80	D
12	C	35	C	58	B	81	A
13	C	36	B	59	C	82	D
14	D	37	C	60	B	83	B
15	D	38	A	61	B	84	A
16	C	39	A	62	D	85	C
17	C	40	B	63	C	86	B
18	B	41	B	64	C	87	C
19	A	42	D	65	A	88	A
20	B	43	C	66	C	89	B
21	C	44	B	67	C	90	D
22	C	45	A	68	A		
23	A	46	D	69	B		

5 ♦ ₹80,000

1	D	17	A	33	D	49	B
2	B	18	B	34	C	50	C
3	C	19	C	35	C	51	D
4	A	20	C	36	B	52	A
5	B	21	D	37	B	53	B
6	A	22	B	38	D	54	A
7	A	23	B	39	D	55	B
8	D	24	A	40	A	56	B
9	B	25	C	41	B	57	B
10	B	26	D	42	C	58	D
11	A	27	C	43	B	59	C
12	A	28	A	44	D	60	B
13	D	29	D	45	D	61	A
14	B	30	B	46	B	62	A
15	A	31	B	47	C	63	C
16	D	32	B	48	A	64	B

65	C	69	C	73	B	77	D
66	C	70	A	74	D	78	B
67	D	71	B	75	C	79	D
68	B	72	B	76	D	80	C

6 ♦ ₹1,60,000

1	B	21	C	41	A	61	D
2	B	22	C	42	D	62	A
3	C	23	A	43	D	63	C
4	B	24	D	44	B	64	B
5	B	25	A	45	C	65	B
6	C	26	C	46	A	66	C
7	D	27	C	47	A	67	C
8	C	28	C	48	D	68	B
9	A	29	D	49	C	69	A
10	D	30	B	50	B	70	B
11	C	31	C	51	C	71	D
12	D	32	D	52	D	72	B
13	C	33	B	53	C	73	B
14	D	34	D	54	C	74	C
15	B	35	B	55	B	75	D
16	A	36	D	56	B	76	D
17	C	37	B	57	A	77	B
18	A	38	D	58	A	78	A
19	D	39	B	59	D	79	B
20	B	40	A	60	B	80	B

7 ♦ ₹3,20,000

1	B	14	D	27	B	40	A
2	D	15	B	28	D	41	C
3	B	16	D	29	D	42	A
4	C	17	D	30	A	43	A
5	A	18	D	31	B	44	B
6	B	19	C	32	A	45	B
7	C	20	B	33	C	46	C
8	B	21	C	34	B	47	A
9	B	22	B	35	A	48	C
10	D	23	A	36	B	49	B
11	C	24	B	37	C	50	C
12	C	25	A	38	C	51	A
13	C	26	C	39	A	52	B

53	D	60	A	67	D	74	C
54	C	61	C	68	A	75	B
55	B	62	C	69	C	76	B
56	D	63	B	70	B	77	B
57	D	64	A	71	C	78	A
58	C	65	B	72	B	79	C
59	C	66	C	73	B	80	D

8 ◆ ₹6,40,000

1	C	21	B	41	C	61	B
2	B	22	C	42	C	62	C
3	C	23	A	43	B	63	D
4	C	24	B	44	C	64	C
5	D	25	D	45	C	65	B
6	A	26	B	46	B	66	B
7	C	27	B	47	C	67	D
8	C	28	B	48	B	68	C
9	B	29	D	49	D	69	A
10	C	30	B	50	A	70	D
11	C	31	C	51	B	71	B
12	A	32	D	52	D	72	A
13	D	33	A	53	B	73	C
14	C	34	B	54	D	74	A
15	B	35	C	55	B	75	A
16	C	36	D	56	A	76	A
17	B	37	C	57	B	77	C
18	C	38	B	58	C	78	C
19	B	39	B	59	B	79	B
20	D	40	C	60	B	80	C

9 ◆ ₹12,50,000

1	A	13	B	25	B	37	C
2	C	14	A	26	A	38	C
3	A	15	B	27	C	39	C
4	B	16	B	28	C	40	C
5	B	17	C	29	B	41	A
6	C	18	A	30	C	42	C
7	C	19	A	31	B	43	D
8	A	20	B	32	A	44	C
9	A	21	C	33	B	45	C
10	C	22	C	34	A		
11	C	23	C	35	B		
12	B	24	A	36	D		

10 ✦ ₹25,00,000

1	C	11	D	21	C	31	B
2	A	12	D	22	C	32	A
3	C	13	B	23	D	33	B
4	B	14	C	24	C	34	D
5	D	15	D	25	C	35	B
6	C	16	B	26	B	36	C
7	A	17	A	27	B	37	A
8	C	18	B	28	D	38	B
9	B	19	A	29	D	39	C
10	D	20	D	30	B	40	B

11 ✦ ₹50,00,000

1	D	11	C	21	C	31	D
2	C	12	B	22	A	32	B
3	D	13	D	23	C	33	B
4	C	14	B	24	B	34	A
5	B	15	D	25	C	35	A
6	D	16	C	26	B	36	C
7	D	17	D	27	C	37	C
8	B	18	A	28	B	38	D
9	A	19	A	29	A	39	A
10	D	20	B	30	C	40	C

12 ✦ ₹1 Crore

1	D	8	C	15	A	22	C
2	A	9	C	16	B	23	B
3	A	10	A	17	B	24	C
4	C	11	A	18	D	25	B
5	B	12	C	19	B		
6	C	13	A	20	A		
7	D	14	A	21	B		

Score Sheets

Write your name and the names of any other contestants in the space provided. Shade in each of the boxes lightly with a pencil once you or one of your fellow contestants has won the amount in that box. If you or any of the other contestants answer & question incorrectly and are out of the game, use a soft eraser to rub out the relevant boxes so that the final score is showing.

SCORE SHEET

contestant's name		contestant's name	
50:50 ☐	👥 ☐	☎ ☐	50:50 ☐	👥 ☐	☎ ☐

12	₹ 1 CRORE	12	₹ 1 CRORE
11	₹ 50,00,000/-	11	₹ 50,00,000/-
10	₹ 25,00,000/-	10	₹ 25,00,000/-
9	₹ 12,50,000/-	9	₹ 12,50,000/-
8	₹ 6,40,000/-	8	₹ 6,40,000/-
7	₹ 3,20,000/-	7	₹ 3,20,000/-
6	₹ 1,60,000/-	6	₹ 1,60,000/-
5	₹ 80,000/-	5	₹ 80,000/-
4	₹ 40,000/-	4	₹ 40,000/-
3	₹ 20,000/-	3	₹ 20,000/-
2	₹ 10,000/-	2	₹ 10,000/-
1	₹ 5,000/-	1	₹ 5,000/-

SCORE SHEET

contestant's name	contestant's name
....	....
50:50 ⬤⬤ ⬘	50:50 ⬤⬤ ⬘
☐ ☐ ☐	☐ ☐ ☐

12	₹ 1 CRORE	12	₹ 1 CRORE
11	₹ 50,00,000/-	11	₹ 50,00,000/-
10	₹ 25,00,000/-	10	₹ 25,00,000/-
9	₹ 12,50,000/-	9	₹ 12,50,000/-
8	₹ 6,40,000/-	8	₹ 6,40,000/-
7	₹ 3,20,000/-	7	₹ 3,20,000/-
6	₹ 1,60,000/-	6	₹ 1,60,000/-
5	₹ 80,000/-	5	₹ 80,000/-
4	₹ 40,000/-	4	₹ 40,000/-
3	₹ 20,000/-	3	₹ 20,000/-
2	₹ 10,000/-	2	₹ 10,000/-
1	₹ 5,000/-	1	₹ 5,000/-